POVERTY & HEALTH

Reaping a Richer Harvest

Marie-Thérèse Feuerstein

MACMILLAN

First published 1997 by
MACMILLAN EDUCATION LTD
London and Basingstoke
Companies and representatives throughout the world

ISBN 0–333–66130–3

10   9   8   7   6   5   4   3   2   1
06 05 04 03 02 01 00 99 98 97

This book is printed on paper suitable for recycling and
made from fully managed and sustained forest sources.

Typeset by EXPO Holdings, Malaysia

Printed in Hong Kong

A catalogue record for this book is available from the
British Library.

Acknowledgements
The author and publishers wish to acknowledge, with thanks, the following
artwork and photographic sources:
Artwork
Victoria Francis chapter headings, pp. 15–16
Boy Domingus p. 77
Emilio Rivero III pp. 7, 93
South–South Solidarity p. 125
TEAR Fund p. 119
Other artwork is by Maggie 'Manisha' Claringbull
Copyright for artwork by Maggie Claringbull, Victoria Francis and Emilio
Rivero is held by the author
Photographs
Behrhorst Clinic Foundation Inc. p. 23
Marie-Thérèse Feuerstein pp. 100, 150
Panos Illustrations cover
John and Penny Hubley cover
Intermediate Technology cover

The author and publishers have made every effort to trace the copyright holders,
but if they have inadvertently overlooked any they will be pleased to make the
necessary arrangements at the first opportunity.

Cover illustration by Marie-Thérèse Feuerstein and Maggie Claringbull.

POVERTY
&HEALTH

Reaping a Richer Harvest

To Ruth and John,
Thanks for your help,
Warmest wishes,

Jerusalem 7 September 1997

Contents

FOREWORD
AND ACKNOWLEDGEMENTS

Writing this book has brought back powerful memories of time spent living and working directly with people who are poor. In the late sixties this involved living with the poor in their houses, sleeping in hammocks and eating mostly manioc flour. In the seventies it involved sleeping on mats on earthen floors, eating maize pancakes and beans, and getting up at night to light a fire if it was too cold. In the eighties and nineties it involved sleeping in places where the mosquitoes were voracious, eating rice and lentils, using pit latrines and washing in buckets or rivers.

Living with the poor involved sharing their problems. These included coping with people who were sometimes violent or drunk, some who were fearful of oppressive landowners or the military, and those mourning loved ones – some killed in peasant massacres. Yet there were many happy moments of warmth, companionship, humour and generosity from individuals, despite their own deprivations. There were joyful celebrations of births and marriages, and colourful local festivals with music and dancing. Above all, there was compassion and courage, and a realisation that we were brothers and sisters who shared a common humanity. What I could have taught them was nothing by comparison with what they taught – and continue to teach – me.

This book was written over a period of two years, parts of it in places ranging from forested tropical mountains to deserted airport lounges, hotel rooms and crowded libraries. Other than an advance of $2000 from the publisher, I was unable to find financial support from any other source. It is perhaps appropriate that a book dealing with poverty should have been written on a shoestring budget and under increasingly difficult and uncertain conditions.

During the writing there have been many colleagues whose encouragement and comments have been appreciated. In 1994–5 Dr Michel Jancloes, director of the World Health Organization's Division of Intensified Cooperation with Least Developed Countries (ICO) and Dr John Martin, deputy director, invited me to work with them on various aspects of poverty and health. From this work developed some of the impetus for this book. Thanks are extended to other WHO staff, including Dr Guy Carrin and Dr Avia Ron of ICO; Dr Gregory Goldstein, director of the 'Healthy Cities' initiative; Dr D. B. Warner and Dr M. Simpson-Hebert of Rural Environmental Health; Dr J. Bertolote of Mental Health Service Development; Dr John Clements of the Global Programme on Vaccines; Dr Socrates Litsios of the Division of Tropical Diseases; and Dr H. L. Friedman and Sr A. Thompson of the Division of Family Health.

Particular thanks are extended to Dr Samuel Kalibala of UNAIDS, who commented on the section dealing with deprivation and AIDS. Appreciation for encouragement and materials is also extended to Dr Hamid Tabatabai of the International Labour Office; Dr Birgitte

Sorensen, director of the War-torn Societies Project of the United Nations Research in Social Development; and Dr Franz Simmersbach of the Food and Agriculture Organization, Rome.

Other colleagues who contributed to the shaping of this book include Diana Smith and Dr Erlinda Senturias of the World Council of Churches in Geneva; Dr Don Clarke of the Commonwealth Foundation; Brian Kerr of the Agricultural Development Unit, Commonwealth Secretariat in London; Dr Hermione Lovel of the University of Manchester (who provided feedback on the lifecycle sections of the book); John Best of the Agricultural and Rural Development Centre, University of Reading (who provided feedback on some of the agricultural and livestock content); Margaret Thomas, health economist (who provided feedback on costs of health care); and Dr Margaret Owen, women and development and human rights lawyer (who found time to advise me on the legal sections, despite final work on her own book *A World of Widows*, published by Zed Press).

Thanks are also extended to Suzanne Fustulkian, co-director of AHRTAG (who commented on the appropriate technology section); Anne-Marie Sharman of Helpage International (who helped shape the section on older people), Dr Peter Poore of Save the Children; Paul Spray and Margaret O'Grady of Christian Aid; Ian Linden of the Catholic Intstitute of International Relations; and Daniel Owen and Meera Shah, who shared experiences of participatory poverty assessment in Africa. Madame M. Albajly of CIMADE in Paris provided information on the trade in body organs of the poor. The cooperation of librarians at the Institute of Development Studies, Sussex and London School of Hygiene and Tropical Medicine was appreciated. Special thanks are extended to Shirley Hamber of the International Department of Macmillan who was particularly supportive during the arduous months of final manuscript production. I am also indebted to Pat Gordon Smith for the editing of this book.

ILLUSTRATIONS

The illustrations for this book were planned with care, but I did not have sufficient funds to cover their cost. The response to my plea for sponsorship of illustrations was deeply appreciated. Almost $1700 was raised. Those who generously contributed include my husband Malcolm, daughter Rachel, son Joseph, and my mother Gwendolyn Wallbridge. Others among my extended family were Cristina and Jeffrey Bayley, Mr and Mrs James Strang, Colonel Clifford Bennett, Gillian Simons, Marie Gumbiner, Benita and Oscar Ferris, Neil and Gilly Ferris. Cousin Margaret and Mamoud Boutorabi enabled two chapters to be illustrated. Mr and Mrs John Olver enabled another whole chapter to be illustrated. Gratitude and appreciation are also extended to Dr Kirsten Borger-Poulsen, Mrs Joan Kitson, Dr and Mrs Karl Hoheneck, Audrey Moser, Sylvia and Roddy MacKenzie, Mr Cecil Greatorex, Margaret Journeaux, John and Catharina Ardagh, Rabbi and Mrs Rolle, Rhonda and Johnathan Apt, Mrs Anne Geller, Beryl Knotts, Dr Charlie Cullen and his wife Karen, Dr and Mrs Michael Vaile, Reverend Dr Peter Blackwell-Smythe, Professor and Mrs Kirshenbaum, Dr Margaret Thomas, Dr Peter Poore, and Dr Chris Rose of Action in International Medicine.

Also deeply appreciated was the support of colleagues and friends from the North Simbu Rural Development Project, Papua New Guinea: Kwame Oduro, Rob Shelton, Dorothea and Andrew Hayton, and sons Sebastian and Jonas – who donated a week's pocket money to fund illustrations. The grant of nearly $800 towards illustrations from Indira Biswas Benbow, administrator of Teaching Aids at Low Cost (TALC) was also greatly appreciated

Special thanks are extended to the illustrators themselves. Chapter headings and some illustrations were provided by Victoria Francis, and cartoons by Emilio Riviero III. Given the extortionate rate being charged commercially for use of photographic materials, I am particularly grateful to John and Penny Hubley for allowing free use of two of their photos. Thanks are also extended to the Behrhorst Clinic Foundation Inc. in the USA, the Panos Institute and South–South Solidarity in India, who enabled me to 'pay' for use of their materials through exchange of my previous book. The TEAR Fund and Intermediate Technology also generously allowed me to use and adapt their photos free of cost. Above all, I owe a great deal to illustrator, Manisha, who has worked steadily with me during the past year. We laboured over the many types of illustrations and tables so that they might be more easily and enjoyably shared with those who use this book.

Finally, the book has two special dedications. First, to the memory of my great cousin Dr Kittie Schudel Van Zwanenberg, who would have found it interesting reading. Second, it is dedicated to health and development workers from many sectors, particularly the younger generations, who continue to battle onwards in their efforts to help those who are poor and vulnerable move out of poverty and attain a better standard of health. They always provoke sensations of admiration, of humility and of hope – because of their courage. Some readers of my previous book have suggested I again include a poem. The one which follows shares some of the practical realities of poverty.

Marie-Thérèse Feuerstein, 1997

RAIN

Will the rain never stop
Unceasingly pouring
In torrents
To soak neath the damp earth,
Cascading from broken-tiled roofs
Filling rusty drums,
Where in the eve of the next day
The people rejoice
At the clearness
Clean softness
Of water unpolluted
By the filth
Of human living.

****

Will the rain never stop
Unceasingly falling
Dripping its damp discomfort
Onto the faces of sleeping children
Huddled for warmth in a woven hammock
The aged face of their young mother
Glows in the smoky circle of light
From the oil lamp on the bark floor
In the heavy night
Giving breast
And love and life
To a slant-eyed baby.

****

Will the rain never stop,
With ruthless intent
Bowing leaf and palm
And the head of a boy
Who struggles to raise
His heavy body from the clutching mud
And falling
Back into the red mass
Mocked by an empty bottle
Half broken by his side.

****

Rain
Unceasingly pouring
With the noise of a million drops
Drumming out of the darkness.
No frogs or owls
Or musicians of the night
Have strength to sing.
But do you hear those cries
Rending even the mighty roar of the rain
As a writhing girl gives birth
After long hours of waiting
Aided in desperation
By the jagged thrust of a rusty blade.

****

Will the rain never stop
In torrents cascading
With ruthless intent destroying
The frail timbered seed box
High from the gound,
Crushing
Enmeshing

Newly born shoots
Green symbol of labour by gnarled hands
Brave attempts to fill swollen bellies
Of raven haired children.

****

The river is rising
Mighty Amazon
Metre by metre
Invading the land
Destroying
Irreplacably
Precious harvest of jute
Planted in sweat
And mud
And the sting
Of a million insects
In the heat of a pitiless sun.

****

The last drops have fallen
Splashing
With malice
The torn clothing
Faded and threadbare
Patched in a dozen colours
Hung in hopefulness to dry
On the skilful curve
Of an upturned canoe.

****

A shaft of moonlight caresses
Innocent faces of children at peace.
A boy sinks to rest
With troubled dreams and poisoned mind
In the darkness above
Glows the smile of a sweat-drenched girl
In the gentle ecstasy of motherhood.

****

Sleep now
In the calm freshness of the night...

****

Marie-Thérèse Feuerstein, Amazonas Brasil 1969.

INTRODUCTION

WHAT IS THIS BOOK ABOUT? WHO IS IT FOR?

Many people working in development already know a great deal about poverty and about the poor, especially those who have been working closely with them for decades. However, new facts and fresh scientific evidence has been emerging on the effects of poverty on health. The main purpose of this book is to share this information in such a way that it can be used to improve strategies for working with and for the poor and vulnerable, where they live and work, whether in remote rural communities or urban neighbourhoods.

Poverty and Health is written particularly for those who work in various fields of development – practitioners, planners, managers and field staff working in rural districts or urban neighbourhoods in developing countries. They include government and non-government health workers, rural or urban extension workers, workers in the private voluntary sector, trainers and researchers. They are involved, or feel the need to become increasingly involved in action against poverty and for health. The book will also be useful for those taking basic or advanced development courses. The participatory development approach – the basis of my first book, *Partners in Evaluation*, which many people in various fields found helpful – has also been applied here to the problems of poverty and health.

PROSPERITY AND POVERTY – SURPRISES AND CHALLENGES

As the turn of the century approaches, greater attention is being paid to poverty, in both developing and industrialised countries. The latter thought their prosperity would banish poverty, but the sad fact is that poverty is also increasing in those countries. Although poverty is experienced differently both in degree and type in developing and developed countries, there are still many similarities in the ways in which poverty undermines health. These have been made worse during the past decade by environmental degradation and the HIV/AIDS pandemic, which have both had a striking influence on the ways in which some people become poor and others become poorer.

Poverty and health are related to so many interconnected factors. This book is about untangling some of them, and reinforcing people's abilities to look at what is causing poverty and ill-health in a particular place. Serious attention needs to be paid to root causes of poverty and broad action is required by politicians and economists to solve some of the root problems of poverty, such as implementing land reform or reducing urban violence. Other action needs to be more narrowly targeted, by taking practical steps in places where the poor live and work. This particular type of action is the main focus of this book.

Large international meetings can only do so much in analysing and re-analysing poverty's causes and consequences. Many meetings seem only to echo the last meeting and one message of this book is that we need to learn how *not* to deal with the problem. Old approaches must be re-examined. New combinations of approach and content are urgently needed.

DESIGNED TO BE USEFUL IN THE FIELD

Poverty and Health is designed to be used as a field handbook as well as a textbook. It includes examples of practical approaches, guidelines and checklists to adapt for use at district, community and particularly household and workplace levels. These include actions which a poor household itself can afford to take in order to promote better health and, particularly, to avoid disease. Examples of participatory planning and monitoring, and of innovative action – all of which have proved useful in the field – are provided. Some approaches which work well on a small scale may not be feasible on a larger scale. Nevertheless other small-scale approaches may be applicable to to the larger scale.

While the main focus of the book is on poverty in developing countries, some of the principles are also valid for industrialised countries. This book is based on over two years of research covering a wide range of countries and projects – from national to local level – and an extensive literature search. The book also reflects the personal experience of the author. Great care has been taken to provide a rich array of illustrations, line drawings, cartoons and photographs, which may be reproduced or adapted by readers for their own needs.

WHAT DOES THIS BOOK CONTAIN?

Chapter 1 looks at what poverty means, and at various types of poverty. It asks who and where are the poor and vulnerable, and whether the poorest are the most vulnerable. It considers why absolute poverty is different from other types of poverty, what are the main types of basic human needs, why there is increasing 'feminisation' of poverty and whether the poor can escape from a poverty cycle. The meaning of poverty lines is explored as are indexes to assess poverty. Lastly, the increasing dimensions of poverty are outlined in various countries and regions of the world.

Chapter 2 suggests a practical and rapid participatory method of 'poverty profiling' which blends existing information with that generated by the poor and vulnerable themselves. Examples are provided of various types of participatory poverty assessment. Next, 20 main causes of poverty that affect the rural and urban poor are considered. The chapter traces links between migration, employment and poverty in relation to health. Lastly, it looks at factors which affect the welfare and health of indigenous peoples.

Chapter 3 outlines the main ways in which poverty affects health. It considers effects of food deprivation, shelter, safe water and sanitation. A life-cycle approach is used to illustrate how poverty affects growth and health at various stages during a human life cycle. For each stage there are examples of preventive or remedial action, and diagrams to use and adapt. Next, the focus is on some diseases and conditions which hit the poor hardest, like malaria, tuberculosis, intestinal helminths (worms), and mental disorder.

Chapter 4 suggests 20 main root causes of poverty, looks at their relationship to health and discusses the feasibility of action against them. The central role of livestock in the survival patterns of the poor is examined, especially issues relating to human and animal health, while access by the poor to simple and appropriate technologies is shown to improve human health and wellbeing. Lastly, there are examples of innovative educational schemes to reach previously unreached children, especially girls, who are poor.

Chapter 5 looks at main policies and laws relating directly or indirectly to the human life cycle in terms of health. It considers how corruption can sabotage such policies and laws, and how some development policies, such as tourism, can have negative effects on the poor and vulnerable. Participatory needs assessment and planning are outlined, with a practical exercise on family needs assessment. The often uneasy fit between bottom-up and top-down planning is briefly examined, and some policy and planning perspectives of NGOs, along with practical suggestions to strengthen the interaction between NGOs and government. The next focus is planning financial services and credit for the poor. Lastly, links are traced between increased income for women and improved family health.

Chapter 6 asks what it really feels like to be poor and explores some neglected psychological aspects of poverty and misconceptions about the poor. It focuses on assets of the poor, both material and human, and how the poor lose those assets, often with profoundly damaging consequences. Links are drawn between survival patterns. Lastly the effects of poverty on family life are explored, especially as they undermine health and survival.

Chapter 7 looks at how damage to natural and man-made environments affects the health and lives of people who are poor. The meaning of sustainable development is explored through looking at air quality, land, food production, forests, wildlife, fresh water, ocean and fishery resources, minerals and metals, and energy use, all of which affect the livelihood and wellbeing of the poor. There are practical suggestions for assessment of a local environment and local action to protect the environment at the same time as protecting human health. Lastly, the focus is on man-made environments of conflict and violence, the way that social decay affects the the poor and vunerable, and the problem of eco-refugees.

Chapter 8 examines the meaning of safety nets, what they need to contain and ways of targeting the poor and vulnerable so that they may benefit. Safety net schemes such as appropriate food schemes are described. Factors undermining the health services themselves are outlined, as is the relationship between poverty and AIDS. A basic index is suggested for assessing coping strategies by poor households. The impact of natural hazards and disasters is considered, and some practical actions to reduce their impact on the poor are suggested. Lastly, the question of coping with disabilities is explored.

Chapter 9 considers whether basic health care costs are being shifted to the poor, and looks at the costs of an essential minimum health package. Cost recovery and user fees are considered as they affect the poor, as is the question of fee exemption. Next, the chapter focuses on what poor households are actually spending on health – and disease. Lastly, the discussion turns to the types of health financing mechanisms which are being used to support primary health care, such as revolving funds, health insurance and credit schemes.

Chapter 10 emphasises the importance of designing, monitoring and evaluation systems with the poor, including selection of simple poverty and health-focused indicators. Examples are provided of participatory approaches and tools to use and adapt, including visual methods for non-literates, improved local financial accounting and community monitoring boards. Lastly, there are suggestions for using experiences of smaller projects to improve action against poverty and to improve health of the poor. A glossary and a list of references is included.

HOW MUCH DO WE REALLY KNOW ABOUT POVERTY?

What does *poverty* mean? How many types of poverty are there, and what are their main causes? Who are the poor, the disadvantaged and the vulnerable? Are the poor always vulnerable and are the vulnerable always poor? This chapter sets the scene for looking at poverty and health by exploring some basic common assumptions about poverty and the poor. It focuses on absolute poverty – and why it is different from other types of poverty. What is *deprivation* and what are *basic human needs*? Where did the idea of basic needs come from? What types of basic needs do people have and why are the poor more vulnerable to denial of basic needs? Why are women and children particularly affected by poverty? Can people escape from a *cycle of poverty*? Who decides how many people are below a *poverty line* and how are such lines drawn? How can *indexes of deprivation* be used to activate action against poverty and for health? Finally, the chapter sketches the present increasing dimensions of poverty in various countries and regions of the world.

1.1 WHAT DOES POVERTY MEAN?

In this book, poverty means being in want of the essential elements to sustain human life and human health. It means experiencing scarcities and deficiencies.

1.2 MANY TYPES OF POVERTY

There are many types of poverty in a single society. Each has to be considered separately from the others, so that the causes and effects of each type are clear. This enables more effective actions to prevent and tackle poverty.

Poverty falls into the types that are given below, along with their main causes.

1 **Inherited poverty.**
Poor parents pass on their poverty to their children. It can be part of a seemingly unending poverty cycle.

2 **Instant poverty.**
Sudden hazards and circumstances like earthquakes, typhoons, drought, bankruptcy, war and refugee movements.

3 **Temporary poverty.**
Caused by some of the same hazards as create instant poverty, but lasting a shorter time, for instance rains come, loans are obtained, war ceases.

4 **New poverty.**
Income/savings of workers and pensioners are eroded by high unemployment, inflation rates, or small cash-crop farmers are ruined by high input costs and low prices of agricultural products.

5 **Relative poverty.**
Deprivation of opportunities, material assets and self respect regarded as normal in the community to which people belong. For example people may be adequately fed and basically housed, but lack material possessions, educational opportunities and so on.

6 **Absolute poverty.**
Deprivation of elements necessary to sustain life and health, such as adequate food, safe drinking water, shelter, land, employment and personal security. The absolute poor are more likely to keep returning to a state of poverty despite improvements in society, such as better market conditions.

7 **Hidden poverty.**
Can be similar to relative poverty in that people may have adequate food and shelter, but lack other basic needs, such as sufficient heat in cold weather or access to health care and do not report such needs. Also, deprivation of remote populations may be 'hidden'.

8 **Endemic poverty.**
Caused by low productivity and poor resource base, reflected by low income, poor nutrition and health, often affecting smallholders on rain-fed farmlands, displaced banana workers, small-scale fishermen and herders.

9 **Overcrowding poverty.**
Population is heavily concentrated into area of high density, for instance rural Bangladesh.

10 **Terminal poverty.**
Those who are poor both at the beginning and the end of their lives.

1.3 IDENTIFYING THE POOR AND THE VULNERABLE

The poor and vulnerable people are most likely to be the landless or small landowners (owning less than three hectares of cropland), small-scale artisans and traders, female-headed households, low-wage workers, the unemployed, marginalised indigenous populations, nomadic herdsmen, pastoralists, small-scale fishermen, refugees and displaced people. But even among the poor there are 'the poorest of the poor' who are most vulnerable to the ravages of ill health, such as landless female-headed households that are without any cropland.

Being vulnerable means being exposed to potential injury and damage, and vulnerability to further harm is particularly acute for those who have been injured or damaged already. The most vulnerable in a population are those for whom multiple deprivations converge, such as lack of food, shelter, safe drinking water, health care, education and employment. They suffer from lack of assets, items and opportunities which land and money can provide. This is a condition of *absolute vulnerability*. For such people, the challenges of daily survival are endless and achieving a reasonable standard of health is difficult.

In any place, the most vulnerable group is likely to be in the lower half of the population segment below the poverty line, or in the last fifth of the total population ranked according to specific poverty indicators. Close to the absolutely poor and vulnerable are the relatively vulnerable, who are almost as badly off and likely to slide – or be propelled into – absolute poverty. Some people tend to move in and out of the poverty groups as their socio–economic environment changes, but the most vulnerable are those who persistently fall below the poverty line. Sometimes the poorest of the poor lose their fragile grip on the poverty line.

Are the poorest of the poor more sick than other poor?

The poorest and most vulnerable population groups often have the worst health indicators. For example, in 1990 the maternal mortality rate (women who die of complications in pregnancy and childbirth) in Guatemala, Central America was 243 per 100 000 births among the remoter indigenous Indian population, compared to the national average of 106 per 100 000 births. Infants and young children who are poor become sick and die more often than those less poor. Adults with diseases like tuberculosis or malaria are more common among the poorest households and those who are poor can be severely disadvantaged when it comes to preventing illness and sustaining health.

Does poverty always make you vulnerable?

Some people who are considered poor in material and even financial assets, such as rural tribal or indigenous people, may be able to meet basic needs such as food, adequate drinking water and locally made shelter. They may be less vulnerable than the urban poor who suffer constant and multiple deprivations such as inadequate food, polluted drinking water and rodent-infested dwellings. Although they may fall into the same per capita income band as the urban non-indigenous poor, they may have better health because of their lifestyles. However, the rural poor may be more vulnerable to violence, such as developers who deprive them of traditional lands. The landless poor of Asia may be vulnerable to many varieties of ill health, as well as to enslaving feudal systems which deprive them of both land and freedom. The type of poverty experienced influences the type and degree of vulnerability which occurs.

Why absolute poverty is different

Absolute poverty is the most severe deprivation of elements necessary to sustain human life and health. Its classification may be based on the cost of a minimum consumption basket containing basic food necessary for the nationally recommended calorie intake, as well as some non-food items such as fuel and blankets. For the absolutely poor even basic items, such as those on the right in the illustration, may be largely beyond their reach.

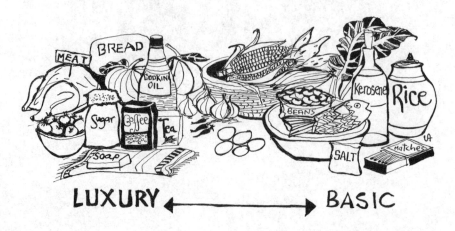

LUXURY ⟵⟶ BASIC

As Robert Macnamara said in an address to the World Bank's board of governors in 1975, being in a state of absolute poverty is in effect life at the margin of existence.

1.4 THE MAIN TYPES OF BASIC HUMAN NEED

Whatever the specifics of locality, the main types of basic need which people have are:

1 **Physical human needs**. Food, safe drinking water, sleep and excretion of human waste products. Activities like cooking, cleaning of the body and washing of clothes.

2 **Psychosocial and spiritual needs**. Affection, sexual relations, sociability, religious practices, privacy, child care, creative pursuits, communications, recreation and entertainment, self-realisation, social participation, human rights and mobility.

3 **Environmental needs**. Protection from extremes of heat and cold, rain and wind, dust, toxic chemicals and other pollutants, insects, rodents and vermin. Also, energy for cooking, lighting, heating and ventilation.

4 **Adequate shelter needs**. Place for protection from environment, such as walls, roofing and personal security. Doors and windows which can be locked. Drainage, disposal of safe human excreta and garbage, energy/fuel. Storage for food, utensils, clothes, personal household and work equipment.

5 **Personal and communal assets**. Access to land and water for home food production, livestock and grazing. Recreational areas and opportunities. Ease of access to roads, transport and markets for sale or exchange of produce. Access to basic education and health services, and to productive employment.

The diagram on p. 10 shows the combination of basic human needs.

Beyond basic needs are other needs, such as for transport – be it a bicycle, bullock cart or truck – and for better quality clothing and household goods, such as a gas stove instead of a kerosene one. In some places it is common to find that poor households will make sacrifices to purchase a television, even if they do not have safe drinking water.

Is a basic need something that a person/household wants – or that they need to sustain life and health? It is not always easy for people to differentiate between what they want and what their basic needs are, particularly for health. Also, there may be conflict in poor households over the varying basic needs. For example, an unemployed father may have a 'basic need' for alcohol and tobacco, leaving little in the household budget with which to purchase food. Poor women usually spend more of their income on child feeding/rearing than the father/partner of the children.

Main types of basic human need

1.5 INCREASING FEMINISATION OF POVERTY

Poverty is hitting increasing numbers of women, and it is hitting them harder. This 'feminisation' of poverty is linked closely to the increase in poor female-headed households, in developing as well as in industrial countries. The percentage of female-headed households varies from the mid teens in some South and Southeast Asian countries, to almost half of all households in some African and Caribbean countries (ILO 1995b). Another indicator of increasing female poverty is that between 1956 and 1988, the number of rural women living below the poverty line rose 51 per cent versus 41 per cent for men (IFAD 1994). Low-income women have sought paid work to compensate for declines in household income. Export promotion policies have raised demand for low-wage female labour. Women have also increased their time spent in unpaid community work to compensate for cutbacks in provision of government services associated with structural adjustment programmes.

The greatest burden of the world economic recession is increasingly borne by those least able to sustain it: women and children. If there was a single action to reverse many of the ill health effects of poverty, it should be to halt this increasing feminisation of poverty. For the poor generally, once caught in the poverty cycle, is there any way out?

1.6 ESCAPING A CYCLE OF POVERTY

The illustration below shows the linked components of a cycle of poverty. The wealthy landlord holds main assets of land and water, along with the key to unlock the chains of poverty which affect human life. To some degree he even has control over animal life.

Chapters 4, 5, and 8 of this book show ways in which the poor can be helped to break out of such a circle of poverty.

1.7 POVERTY LINES

A *poverty line* is a tool for measuring poverty and for separating the poor from the non-poor. Each country defines its own poverty line according to particular circumstances. As well as a poverty line, there is a *poverty front line* – the lowest level of human existence experienced by the absolute poor. To be at this level is to be the poorest of the poor.

A poverty line is constructed according to the value of income or consumption necessary to maintain a minimum standard of human nutrition and other basic necessities. For example, the people living below the poverty line may be regarded in one country as those who earn below the annual average income. In another country, the line may be judged using calorie intake. People living below the poverty line might then be those whose diet falls consistently below the nationally recommended daily calorie intake needed to sustain human life. The most common and most simple measure of poverty, known as the *head count ratio*, simply counts the number of people below a specified poverty line. However, the head count ratio does not show clearly the various levels of poverty within the groups of poor, such as lack of shelter, clothing and other minimum necessities.

Poverty lines do not generally include other factors which determine quality of life, such as access to safe water and basic public services. Some poverty lines are based on the price of basic consumption items required to maintain an average family with a balanced nutritional diet. Generally, there are some hard-core populations always classified as poor, no matter what measures are used. In one Southeast Asian country, the poorest section of the population is considered to be those owning less than 1.5 acres of land, and who have to sell their labour for at least 90 days a year.

Rural and urban poverty line differences

Even within the same country there may be important rural and urban differences. Poverty lines, to be effective, should reflect differences in the cost of living across dates and regions, and should have the same purchasing power. For example, the equivalent of US$2 may purchase some kilos of rice, maize or cassava in both rural and urban areas. But in a rural area it may be cheaper, so there may be money left to purchase a bar of soap and a little kerosene. On this basis, in reality, the urban dweller may be 'poorer'. However, this analysis may be further complicated where there are public subsidies for basic food commodities. Different population groups spend different amounts on food. Calorific intake is generally higher in rural than urban areas because people typically consume high calorie foods as basic.

It has been suggested that a higher poverty line should be drawn for urban than rural populations because it may be easier to become poor in urban than in rural areas. For example, food may cost more in urban areas. On the other hand, poor migrants from rural areas may be better off in their new urban environment, even if they are classified as contributing to increasing urban poverty. They may have risen above the rural poverty line, but still be below the urban poverty line even though they are actively better off.

The situation of most households just above the poverty line is not very different from those below it. Conditions fluctuate. There are hard times and better times. In urban areas, poverty levels change drastically with change in poverty measure used, suggesting that the poor are not easy to identify.

Drawing poverty lines

When constructing and using poverty lines, it may be useful to remember three questions:

1   How should a standard of living be measured?
    Consumption data (the amount which a person/family consumes) may be more constant as a measure because income data may vary according to unemployment or seasonal and migrant labour. Consumption data should include what a household produces (like food crops) as well as what it purchases. However, many aspects of household wellbeing are not clearly revealed by only using consumption and income data as measures. Supplementary data on social outcomes and access to social services are therefore important, such as life expectancy, infant mortality, nutrition, literacy, access to primary education, health services or safe drinking water.

2   Where is the cut-off level below which a family should be considered poor?
    If a poverty line is drawn in such a way that vast numbers of people fall below the line, creating and/or maintaining a social 'safety net' may be regarded as not feasible or affordable (see Chapter 8). Some countries without specifically drawn poverty lines set a proxy poverty line based on minimal food intake in calories, then find the consumption expenditure or income level at which a person typically attains that food intake. A variation on this method is to find the minimum cost of a basic food basket which achieves the necessary energy intake level, then divide this by the share of food in the total actual expenditure of some group of households deemed likely to be poor.

3   How can the depth and severity of poverty be measured?
    What does the severity of poverty depend on? The way the poor are distributed below the poverty line determines the severity in a particular place. For example, there may be vast numbers just below the poverty line or there may be a few just below the line – but vast numbers far below it. For this reason, two poverty lines are sometimes used, an upper and a lower poverty line. This allows better differentiation between the poor and the very poor.

The *poverty gap index* is the difference between the poverty line and the mean (average) income of the poor, expressed as a ratio of the poverty line. It is sometimes called the *income gap ratio*. This can indicate the depth of poverty, but it does not convey the severity of poverty. For example, measuring poverty will be unaffected by a transfer from a poor person to someone who is very poor. What is important is also to be able to understand the way poverty is distributed below the poverty line, and the different degrees of severity with which it affects various population groups. The next section looks briefly at how indexes have been used to assess depth and severity of poverty.

1.8 USING AN INDEX TO ASSESS HUMAN DEPRIVATION, INEQUITY AND SUFFERING

An index is a way of showing the value of something on a scale (a series of degrees or classifications). A poverty index is constructed according to the objectives of the user who might be a researcher, planner or practitioner.

From Experience

In India an index was developed to measure health care use in relation to needs among 606 urban squatter families in Madras. A family level health risk index was constructed combining socio-economic variables of: the most disadvantaged scheduled caste and tribe caste; one or more children under five years of age; all adults in the family being illiterate; only one, or none, of the adult family members being employed; rented housing constructed with non-durable materials and lacking toilet facilities; unprotected source of drinking water; and use of both tobacco and alcohol by a family member. A high risk score of one was assigned to each variable, (high risk = score of 5+).

The index was used to identify high risk families for targeting them with basic health and social services, and to design inputs around their needs, such as improvements in family health, nutrition, improved housing, water and sanitation (Srilatha & Aitken 1991). Researchers in Kenya used a similar risk approach to define health needs, particularly households at risk of childhood mortality.

606 HIGH RISK FAMILIES:

UNPROTECTED DRINKING WATER	75%
ONE OR NO WORKING ADULTS	58%
WITH UNDER FIVES	48%
LOWEST CASTES	29%
USES TOBACCO/ALCOHOL	27%
NO LITERATE ADULTS	21%
POOR HOUSING/NO TOILET	8%

1.9 INCREASING NUMBER OF PEOPLE BELOW THE LINE

It is estimated that 1.3 billion people – more than a fifth of all people in the world – live in poverty. A World Bank report, using a poverty line of an annual per capita income of $370 (1985 US dollars), estimated that in 1990 there were 1.1 billion people in developing countries below the poverty line. The gap between the richest 20 per cent of the world's population and the poorest 20 per cent has more than doubled in the past 30 years, with 85 per cent of world income now going to the richest 20 per cent. The share of the poorest 20 per cent has fallen from 2.3 per cent to 1.4 per cent (Jacobs 1996).

AFRICA

	1980 Urban (%)	1980 Rural (%)	1990 Urban (%)	1990 Rural (%)
Angola	—	—	—	65
Burkino Faso	—	—	—	90
Congo	—	—	—	80
Ethiopia	60	—	60[†]	65[†]
Ghana	59	—	59[†]	37[†]
Guinea	—	—	—	70
Kenya	10	55	10[†]	55[†]
Mozambique	—	—	40	70
Senegal	—	—	—	70
Tanzania	10	60	—	—
Uganda	—	—	25	33
Zambia	26	80	40[*]	—
Zimbabwe	—	—	—	60

MIDDLE EAST

	1980 Urban (%)	1980 Rural (%)	1990 Urban (%)	1990 Rural (%)
Algeria	20	—	20[†]	25
Egypt	30	30	34	34
Iran	13	38	—	—
Iraq	—	40	—	—
Syria	—	60	—	54

ASIA PACIFIC

	1980 Urban (%)	Rural (%)	1990 Urban (%)	Rural (%)
Bangladesh	66	74	86[†]	86[†]
Bhutan	—	—	—	90
China	2	28	0.4[*]	12
India	47	53	37	39
Indonesia	29	28	20	16
Laos	—	—	—	85
Malaysia	13	37	13[†]	38[†]
Nepal	22	36	55[†]	61[†]
Pakistan	23	38	32[†]	29[†]
Philippines	32	41	52[†]	64[†]
Sri Lanka	20	27	15	36
Thailand	8	27	10[†]	25[†]
Vietnam	—	—	—	60

LATIN AMERICA

	1980 Urban (%)	Rural (%)	1990 Urban (%)	Rural (%)
Bolivia	34	81	54	76
Brazil	24	55	33	63
Colombia	13	58	32[†]	70[†]
Costa Rica	10	18	18[†]	20[†]
Dominican Republic	45	43	45[†]	43[†]
El Salvador	24	51	42	51
Guatemala	36	53	61[†]	85[†]
Haiti	72	91	80	99
Honduras	39	71	31[†]	70[†]
Mexico	9	18	9	32
Nicaragua	24	52	58	76
Peru	49	73	46	83[†]

Sources for all tables: International Labour Office Report 1995, except:
   † UNICEF (1996), Latest figures are for 1989;
   * HABITAT (1996), figure for Zambia is 1993.

The greatest increase in human poverty is occurring within developing countries. They contain larger populations, which are growing faster. The tables on pp. 15–16 show the population in poverty as a percentage of the rural and urban population for 1980 and 1990.

DEVELOPING EUROPE

	% in poverty	Date
Hungary	15.4	1991
Poland	22.7	1987
Yugoslavia (former)	24.5	1987

For comparison, examples are included from what is being called developing Europe. Unfortunately, the ILO figures do not include figures for western industrialised countries (Ferge 1991) but in the United Kingdom around 22 per cent of the population were reckoned to be living in poverty in 1988–9 (Blackburn 1993).

Looking at trends in poverty

Poverty is spreading like a disease. The following tables (Jazairy *et al.* 1992) show the incidence of poverty, both rural and urban, in developing countries.

THE INCIDENCE OF RURAL POVERTY IN DEVELOPING COUNTRIES

Country group	Year	Incidence of poverty (%)
Sub-Saharan Africa	1988	60
Asia	1988	31
Asia (ex. China & India)	1988	46
Near East & North Africa	1988	26
Latin America/Caribbean	1988	61
Developing countries	1988	36
Least developed countries	1988	69

INCIDENCE OF URBAN POVERTY IN DEVELOPING COUNTRIES

Country group	Year	Incidence of poverty (%)
Africa	1985	29
Asia (ex. China)	1985	34
Latin America	1985	32
Developing countries (ex. China)	1985	32

The next table (World Bank 1993a) illustrates the global incidence of poverty, including in developing areas of Europe.

OVERALL INCIDENCE OF POVERTY IN DEVELOPING COUNTRIES

Country group	Year	Incidence of poverty (%)
Sub-Saharan Africa	1990	47.6
East Asia	1990	11.6
South Asia	1990	49.0
Middle East & North Africa	1990	33.1
Latin America & Caribbean	1990	25.5
Eastern Europe	1990	7.1
Developing countries	1990	29.7

The final table indicates the cumulative percentage of population in developing world regions under a consumption level equivalent to US$50 per person per month in 1985 and 1990 (Chen *et al.* 1993).

PEOPLE BELOW CONSUMPTION LEVEL OF (a) US$40 PER PERSON PER MONTH (b) US$21 PER PERSON PER MONTH

Region	1985 (%)	1990 (%)
East Asia	(a) 29.94	26.81
	(b) 4.89	4.86
South Asia	(a) 75.31	74.59
	(b) 37.01	33.64
Latin America	(a) 31.97	37.01
	(b) 13.23	17.21
Sub-saharan Africa	(a) 67.01	67.10
	(b) 33.34	34.53
Middle East & North Africa	(a) 75.31	74.59
	(b) 1.33	0.54

The next chapter considers practical approaches to poverty profiling at country level, in order to understand more about poverty and to be able to strengthen planning for action against poverty and for health.

POVERTY PROFILING AND THE CAUSES OF POVERTY

Poverty profiling blends existing information with that generated by the poor and vulnerable themselves. A set of basic profiling questions are suggested in the course of this chapter and examples are provided of various types of participatory poverty assessment. Next, twenty main causes of poverty are considered, and some characteristics of rural and urban poverty. What happens when people migrate? What kinds of population movements have contributed to the poverty of today? How do employment patterns, as well as unemployment influence the health of the poor? Why are indigenous people so often strangers in their own land, and what are the factors which make them so vulnerable? These questions are considered in the concluding sections of the chapter.

A poverty profile is an analytical tool for rapidly and systematically identifying more clearly the poor, where they live, and what causes and characterises their poverty. It helps to generate a set of information to guide action against poverty and for health. The profiling process begins with defining poverty as it is understood in a particular place and from the point of view of the poor themselves. A poverty profile should reveal the patterns of living and working of the poor and show links between poverty and health. The poverty profile methodology can be adapted for use at national, provincial, district and community level. It can be used during a workshop or adapted for preparing a survey. Above all, poverty profiling is a simple, practical and low-cost tool to guide action against poverty and for health.

2.1 KEY QUESTIONS – THE BUILDING BLOCKS OF POVERTY PROFILING

The basis of poverty profiling is identifying key questions, such as those suggested in Appendix A (see pp. 187–94), which are intended to serve as a guide to identifying the actual questions needed in a particular place. The questions to include in a particular profile depend partly on the objectives and intended outcomes of creating the profile. The intention is to produce a structured yet flexible checklist for assembling fairly rapidly a useful, concise, easily readable profile designed for decision making and action. Each question selected should have an action-oriented final purpose. If the question is 'interesting' but not 'useful', it should not be included.

The questions finally selected can then guide preparations for a participatory poverty assessment (where the poor and vulnerable themselves participate in defining and describing their poverty and its effects on health), or those preparing a profile on poverty and health. The questions in Appendix A have a strong health focus, but other questions can be substituted or added if another main focus is required, such as poverty and environment, or poverty and female-headed households. The questions in Appendix A are arranged in four sections:

- introduction
- identification of the poorest and most vulnerable population groups
- social, political, geographical, ecological, and economic factors affecting such groups
- past, present and future options for action against poverty and for health.

2.2 USING EXISTING INFORMATION FOR POVERTY PROFILING

Two types of survey information can be useful, that emerging from household surveys and community surveys.

Surveys

Household surveys can provide important information about individuals and households, such as location, household composition, income, consumption levels, employment, occupational status, education, nutritional and health status.

Community surveys can provide a better understanding of the social infrastructure and characteristics of community systems, and of the facilities and services available – or not available – to the poor. For example, they might reveal the quality and type of leadership in a community, organised action for development, existence and functioning of schools, health facilities, financial services, agricultural extension, and markets and marketing systems for commodities produced (or capable of being produced) by the poor.

Sometimes a community survey takes place at the same time as a household survey. The combination enables better understanding of links between the causes and consequences of poverty. Sometimes community surveys make use of administrative and institutional records (like school registers or health facility records).

Using other sources of existing information

The following checklist will help in deciding what is available and useful in a particular area:

1. Government reports, such as policies and plans relating to poverty, poverty assessments, reports from ministries such as finance, agriculture, education, industrial development, health, community development and social welfare, and environment.

2. University reports, publications, theses, surveys, needs assessments, participatory rural assessments.

3. UN Agency reports.

4. International Non-governmental organisation (NGO) reports.

5. National NGO reports, for instance those put together by national groups such as lawyers, trades unions or professional organisations working in areas relevant to poverty.

6. Published articles relating to poverty in that country in national or international academic journals/newsletters.

7. Published articles/features appearing in national and local newsletters/newsheets.

8. Press articles and letters relating to poverty.

9. Unpublished materials such as letters or notes.

10. Maps relating to poverty in the country which might indicate poorest regions, refugee movements, drought, soil and forest degradation.

11. Photographic, video, film, audio tape, and other audio-visual materials.

12. Other sources of information.

Using a combination of sources

In Malawi, three types of information were used to reveal the situation facing three types of poor households. The first were smallholders – householders with small land holdings. For them, an agricultural census and yearly update provided information on income and family size, and a sample survey provided information on household expenditure. For the second type of household, workers on agricultural estates, a special small survey was carried out. For the third group, urban households, a national urban income-expenditure survey, though not current, provided useful information. In addition, information was used from a population census.

The poverty profiling revealed that around half the population was below a poverty line based on minimum nutritional requirements, and 20 per cent of the population were the 'poorest of the poor'. These were mostly rural smallholders, often female-headed households, heavily reliant on home agriculture (70 per cent), casual farm and non-farm labour, and migrant labour remittances. More than 65 per cent of their household expenditure was on food, they faced the greatest risks of malnutrition and had limited access to health, social services and education.

Using an index of deprivation in poverty profiling

In Nepal, four variables were used to construct an index of deprivation intended to reveal spacial poverty related to degree of remoteness of the poor, location of particular pockets of poverty and need for action against poverty, such as building infrastructure and roads. Each variable was given a particular score. Lowest scores indicated poorest and most vulnerable villages.

Using a participatory approach, a simple index of deprivation can be designed at community level, by the poor themselves and their collaborators. In Chapter 10 there are indicators of poverty and health which can be used to develop such a community-based index of deprivation. For example, communities may decide that any family who eats less than twice a day, has holes in their roof and young children who are not fully immunised, rate high on their own index of deprivation, that is they need help – and they need it quickly.

At whatever level poverty profiling takes place, decisions will have to be made as to the purposes of profiling, location (communities/area/district), costs, materials to be collected or prepared, and who will be involved as facilitators and/or researchers. Those who will be involved need to come from various development sectors because tackling poverty and problems of ill health requires multisectoral action.

2.3 USING THE POVERTY PROFILE AT NATIONAL LEVEL

If poverty is to be discussed at national level by, for instance, policy makers, planners and practitioners, the profile questions can be printed or written on overhead transparencies during a case study/workshop. Optimally, participants appoint a chairman and a rapporteur to steer the case study or workshop. This is important because it is easy to digress when talking about poverty. Particular people or groups can be delegated responsibility to complete certain sections of the profile.

From Experience

In Guatemala, Central America, a group of senior professionals from various ministries and international agencies prepared a poverty profile in 1993. They found that around 80 per cent of the population was living in poverty, the poorest being small farmers concentrated in rural and highland areas. The indigenous population (58 per cent), was largely non-literate and unable to access markets and credit. There was also extreme poverty in slum areas of cities. Infant mortality was 65/1000 live births, but 200/1000 among the indigenous population (1989). Especially vulnerable were indigenous pregnant and lactating women. Three quarters of indigenous pre-school children suffered from chronic malnutrition. Only 25 per cent of rural families had safe water.

The poverty profile was used to guide decisions about future action against poverty and for health.

Sensitivities about information

The information in the Guatemalan example is drawn from multiple sources, including non-governmental ones. One problem in poverty profiling is that there is often conflicting information on origin and causes of poverty in a particular place – depending on who is providing the information. What finally gets into the poverty profile may be influenced by who is preparing it. If it is a government group there may be little information from non-government sources if that is regarded as politically sensitive.

Poverty and the poor are often seen as political issues. In poverty profiling threading a way through such pitfalls is not easy. The main thing is to do it without treachery to those who are poor and vulnerable.

Preparing a report of a poverty profile

When reporting the findings and conclusions of poverty profiling, it can be useful to include illustrations and photographic materials to emphasise certain issues and points. A good local illustrator or cartoonist can often convey key points in a more sharply focused way. People tend to remember pictures and cartoons. Pictures/cartoons can also be turned later into illustrative materials for less literate or non-literate audiences.

2.4 POVERTY PROFILING AT DISTRICT LEVEL

District authorities need to be committed to a district poverty profiling approach if it is to succeed. They may at first be unsure about poverty profiling, perhaps seeing it as likely to produce too much evidence of local deficiencies in provision of services. The results of poverty profiling may not be acceptable to local elites such as landowners or urban employers. In some places, upsetting the status quo has resulted in conflict and violence.

Usually, there is less existing information about poverty at district level than at provincial or national level (excluding the important raw data from service and institutional records). There will be practical issues to consider, such as availability of paper, electricity, transport, fuel, distances, seasons and availability of computers (if used). The best information on the poor and vulnerable will come from the poor and vulnerable themselves.

2.5 HELPING THE POOR TO ANALYSE THEIR OWN SITUATION

There have been many approaches over the past decades to help the poor assess their situation and needs. Some approaches have been local and small scale, others larger. The table on page 25 sets out a range of participatory poverty assessment methods by which the poor have been helped to assess their own situation. It relates issues they looked at with the participatory methods they used. The rest of this section provides brief descriptions of some of the methods.

Wellbeing and wealth ranking

Community members use cards to rank households who have the smallest fields, no cattle or access to ploughing team, fish using baskets only, have no boats, dress poorly, are led by women who are widowed or divorced. These can be compared with those who have assets/wealth like the largest fields, who use fishing nets, can afford to dress well, or give to those who are poorer.

From Experience

Children in Uganda drew their impression of the difference between wealthy and poor people. 'Rich people,' they explained, 'sleep on a bed and own many things, such as spoons, cups, plates. They can afford shoes and handbags, and have cars which look like buses because they have to fit the whole family.'

PARTICIPATORY POVERTY ASSESSMENT – SOME METHODS BY WHICH THE POOR HAVE BEEN ANALYSING THEIR OWN SITUATION

Issues they looked at	Methods they used
Perceptions and indicators of wealth, wellbeing and poverty.	Wellbeing and wealth ranking, social mapping.
Vulnerability, powerlessness, differences in perception by gender.	Semi-structured interviews.
Perceptions of change over time in welfare, terms of trade, access to income and employment.	Time lines, matrix for scoring changes over time (labour market, migration). Trend analysis.
Access/use of services (health, education, credit), perceptions of services and change.	Institutional diagramming, semi-structured interviews. Trend analysis of health, education, marketing services.
Seasonal stress, food security, health, income, expenditure, occupation.	Seasonal calendar (by occupation, residence, income, expenditure, health, food security, access to fuel, water, bad/good years), family needs focusing exercise.
Assets of poor households, such as common property, services natural resources.	Resource mapping, focus groups, institutional diagramming.
Assets of urban households.	Wealth ranking and grouping. Livelihood analysis.
Survival strategies in time of crisis.	Livelihood analysis, semi-structured interviews, ranking exercises.
Perceptions of consumption level of food, clothing, wellbeing.	Wellbeing grouping and/or ranking, social mapping, semi-structured interviews.
Local self-help institutions and support for poor (e.g. market trader associations, churches).	Institutional mapping, semi-structured interviews.
Community 'safety nets' for rural poor.	Institutional mapping, semi-structured interviews.
Role of community institutions in service and infrastructure provision.	Semi-structured interviews. Institutional mapping.
Responsibilities and obligations within households (food, payment of school fees, by gender).	Semi-structured interviews.
Long-term environmental trends e.g. soil and forest degradation, declining rainfall.	Resource mapping at different points in time. Trend analysis.

(References: research on poverty and health in 1995/6; participatory poverty assessment in Africa supported by the World Bank in 1993/4.)

Social mapping

A group of women draw a map on the ground then, individually, standing at the place where their house is located, they talk of their problems and needs, such as having no food, caring for grandchildren, selling chickens to raise school fees or having imprisoned relatives.

Time lines

A person lists, chronologically, crops grown, food availability and consumption, beginning from the time he/she was born. He/she continues to trace the situation as prevailing by school age, such as a drought/flood/changes in farming inputs and outputs, changes in government agricultural policy, road construction, local access to credit, cooperative production, prices of fertiliser or increase in poverty and hunger. What emerges is local perceptions of key changes over time.

Institutional diagramming

A large circle is drawn on the ground/board and community participants are asked to draw certain local 'institutions', using circles of various size (depending on importance). Possible 'institutions' might include headman/leader, rice mill/grinding mill, well/river, traditional birth attendant, school, church, shop/store, clinic/hospital, road, agricultural extension workers. Institutions placed inside the large circle indicate accessibility to the community, or outside the circle indicate that they are less accessible.

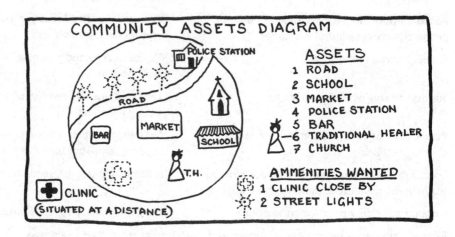

Seasonal calendar

A focus group looks at the pattern of household food security during an average year. This type of calendar can be a matrix with specific local food staples listed to the left and vertical columns for each month of the year. Each household which has access to specific foods at specific times is marked with a dot. A pattern of volume of households by type of food and season emerges across the matrix. (This can also be made, where desired, into a simple graph, which includes incidence of local diseases/conditions like malaria during the rainy season, increased child malnutrition during the lean season). Another type of matrix can list individual diseases and then the incidence of those diseases can be marked (with dots according to number of cases) across the 12 columns of the months of the year. The matrix can be drawn on the ground or blackboard.

SEASONALITY AND DISEASE												
DISEASE	JAN	FEB	MAR	APR	MAY	JUN	JUL	AUG	SEP	OCT	NOV	DEC
MALARIA	∴	∵	∴	∴	∴	∴	∴	∴	∴			
COLDS/COUGHS	∵	∵	∴	∴	∴	∴∴	∴	∴	∴			
DIARROHEA		∵	∴	∴	∴	∴	∴	∴	∴			
SCABIES	∴∴	∴∴	∴∴	∴	∴∴	∴∴	∴∴	∴∴				

Resource mapping

A map is made of the area and marked according to where different natural resources are found, like types of trees (to provide firewood, fruits), forested areas, endangered animals, rivers, wells, swamps, areas which get flooded, fishes, grazing areas for livestock, cropland, soils which are too poor for cultivation or soils which are water loaded.

Livelihood analysis

A group uses beans/grains of rice to record each **expenditure** item (like buying maize/rice/corn/vegetables, or paying school fees) and **income** item (like selling maize/corn/rice/vegetables, beer, roadside food, woven baskets). They place the beans/rice grains on a matrix (drawn on ground/ blackboard) at the relevant place (on vertical columns representing 12 months of the year) where the expenditure or income occurs.

Ranking exercises

A group of women records how treatment is obtained for common diseases like sore eyes, tuberculosis, AIDS, skin conditions, cholera or boils. The diseases/conditions are listed to the left and the treatment options (clinic, home, friends, traditional healer) displayed horizontally in relation to options in vertical columns.

Family needs focusing exercise

A visual participatory exercise, with rural/urban households/community representatives/extension workers/health workers and volunteers, during which an empty blackboard/large piece of paper is gradually filled by participants as they construct and draw (in the centre) an average local family and identify and draw their basic needs, including primary health care needs (see Chapter 5).

Some of the local causes of poverty may be well defined by poor people themselves. But, some of the main root causes of poverty may not be brought out clearly.

2.6 WHAT ARE THE MAIN CAUSES OF POVERTY?

The following illustrations can be adapted, enlarged, and cut into picture cards for various uses, such as stimulating discussion, ranking the causes by importance, guiding feasible action and tracing links between causes of poverty and poverty and health.

Cause		Example
(1)		Most money and assets are concentrated in a few hands – the poor majority have little money or few assets.
(2)		Cuts in labour force and lack of productive employment prevent the poor from rising out of poverty, and accelerate others falling into poverty.
(3)		Small plots of poor farmers are inadequate for livelihood and landless households cannot grow food.
(4)		Few credit sources/only extortionate interest rates available to the poor wanting to start small business.
(5)		Ex-colonial power ignores local concerns about undersea nuclear testing.
(6)		Poor producers get minimal return to increase profit of multinational companies.
(7)		Cuts in social sectors result in hospital/clinic/mobile patrol closures.
(8)		Little access by poor households to benefits of mechanisation and modern technology.
(9)		The votes of the poor sought during election time, but promises unfulfilled, or access to free voting denied.
(10)		Fear and lack of access to legal system continue/increase oppression of the poor.

(11) 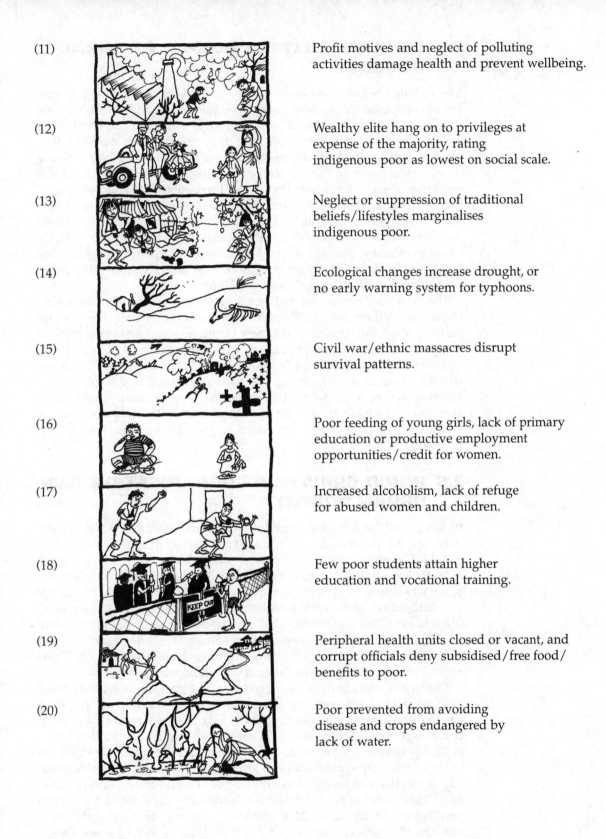 Profit motives and neglect of polluting
activities damage health and prevent wellbeing.

(12) Wealthy elite hang on to privileges at
expense of the majority, rating
indigenous poor as lowest on social scale.

(13) Neglect or suppression of traditional
beliefs/lifestyles marginalises
indigenous poor.

(14) Ecological changes increase drought, or
no early warning system for typhoons.

(15) Civil war/ethnic massacres disrupt
survival patterns.

(16) Poor feeding of young girls, lack of primary
education or productive employment
opportunities/credit for women.

(17) Increased alcoholism, lack of refuge
for abused women and children.

(18) Few poor students attain higher
education and vocational training.

(19) Peripheral health units closed or vacant, and
corrupt officials deny subsidised/free food/
benefits to poor.

(20) Poor prevented from avoiding
disease and crops endangered by
lack of water.

2.7 LOOKING A LITTLE DEEPER AT RURAL POVERTY

Many of the rural poor live in areas of extreme environmental fragility, particularly exposed to the dangers of soil erosion. Without capital, they are frequently unable to invest in even traditional methods of soil and water conservation, and without fallow land, they are forced to shorten fallow periods, putting further strain on the resource base. The rural population in many places used to have a stable relationship with fragile ecological resources. The challenge is to find ways of re-establishing and building on that relationship (Jazairy *et al.* 1992). The rural poor may benefit little from government policies such as food subsidies on imported food, subsidies for industrialisation, and public sector expenditure. These may benefit the urban poor more. In many developing countries, exports are agricultural goods produced by small farmers. Cheap food imports depress the prices paid to small farmers for their own food crops.

The rural poor are surrounded by a dense network of factors which tend to perpetuate their poverty. These include traders and money lenders capitalising upon the economic weakness of the poor and engaging them in unequal exchanges. Rural families who are poor still tend to want many children, largely to supply their labour needs. While the rural share of the world's population is declining, the rural population is still growing in absolute numbers. In the next 20 years the world's rural population is expected to increase by 423 million people. Over the same period, the world's urban population is expected to increase by almost 1.5 billion people.

2.8 RAPID GROWTH OF URBANISATION AND URBAN POVERTY

By the end of the nineteenth century, cities had existed for 6000 years, but only one, an imperial city in China, had reached the size of a million people. Urbanisation, as we know it today, began with the European industrial revolution. By 1900 an estimated 10 per cent of the world's population was urban. By 1950 it had risen to almost 30 per cent, and there were 26 metropolitan areas with populations of two million people or more (Population Crisis Committee 1987). In 1993 there were 33 metropolitan areas with five million people or more. Some 58 of the world's largest metropolitan areas are in developing countries. Nine of them are in China and another nine in India (Population Crisis Committee 1987).

The largest cities in developing countries are growing faster than those in industrialised countries ever did. London, which was the first industrial city to reach a population of one million, took 130 years to reach a population of eight million. By contrast, Mexico City's population stood at only a million people just 50 years ago – and now it stands at 20 million. Cities in the industrialised world have been growing at a rate of 0.8 per cent annually, but in the developing world they grow at a rate of 3.6 per cent annually. This represents a population doubling time for their urban populations of less than 20 years! Also, Africa's urban population is growing at 5 per cent annually, a doubling time of only 12 years. By the year 2010, half of the world's people may live in cities. By 2025 Africa's urban population may be three times the size of North America's.

The slums and shanty towns (peri-urban areas) of developing country cities are growing at twice the rate of cities as a whole. In parts of Latin America these communities are known locally as 'callampas' or mushrooms, because they seem to grow up almost overnight. In 1987, it was estimated that the percentage of urban populations who lived in slums or squatter settlements was more than 30 per cent greater than that for many developing country cities. In some cities, most people lived in the slums, such as in Casablanca (70 per cent), Calcutta (67 per cent), Kinshasa and Bogota (60 per cent), and Mexico City (40 per cent).

Government policies and investments designed to improve life for those who live in slum areas, such as installation of water supplies and sewerage systems, power stations and telephone systems, may largely benefit industrial and commercial interests, and those less poor. Poor slum areas are often just as starved of new investments and services as rural areas. More recently, the major force behind urbanisation is no longer industrialisation. In many developing countries, 60 per cent or more of urban growth results from the excess of urban births over deaths. Forty per cent or less is related to rural–urban migration.

2.9 MIGRATION, POVERTY AND VULNERABILITY

Traditionally, individuals and groups have migrated in search of a new place to live, hunt and have a more sustainable livelihood. More recently, vast numbers have migrated in search of employment. Often, one person who is poor migrates to a city in search of betterment. He/she succeeds and rural relatives later join them in the city. Migrant networks grow in such a way, but it is said that in Africa, increasing poverty is weakening such networks, as urban dwellers cannot afford any more to support poor relatives while they look for work. The shanty towns of the developing world contain the overflow of rural hopes and rural desperation.

Involuntary migration and some historical seeds of poverty

Among the poor in the Americas are descendants of people who found themselves involuntary migrants – through the notorious systems of slavery and indentured labour. Portuguese sailors began to enslave Africans around 1442, transporting them back to Europe for use in their own households. By 1550, the first slave ship sailed from Africa to the West Indies to meet the need for intensive field labour in the sugar and tobacco plantations of the Caribbean (Curtin 1990). Over the next couple of centuries, some 15 million people are thought to have been taken from Africa. Around 13 per cent of them never reached their destination, perishing in cells at the port or in the holds of ships during the sea voyage. Survivors were eventually landed in Brazil, the Caribbean and North America.

Britain, Portugal, France, Holland, the then British United States and Denmark were all involved in this human trade. The economics of slavery were crude. The question was whether to breed slaves or just work them to death and buy new ones. For under the equivalent of today's US$10, an adult slave was sold to a dealer, who then sold the man/woman on the other side of the Atlantic for four times as much. Slaves were worked so hard that they were expected to last around five years.

In 1807, the slave trade was abolished in Britain, due to public pressure, but it was not until 1865 that slavery was abolished in the United States of America. The slave trade was one of the largest mass migrations of labour in human history. Today, it is estimated that around 40 million people in the Americas and Caribbean are descended from slaves. However, even before slavery was abolished it was being replaced by another notorious system – indentured labour.

In the footsteps of slavery – indentured labour

Under this system, workers might sign a contract for a specified number of years to work abroad or they might travel abroad and sign such a contract. Another method was for a foreman to take a gang of workers, lend them money and take them overseas to make them work to pay off the loan. Indentured labourers came mainly from China and India. From about 1830, they were despatched all over the world, to British colonies in North America, Africa and Asia, as well as to French, German and Dutch colonies. They also went to the United States and to newly independent countries of Latin America. As many as 30 000 Chinese workers went to work for Chinese businessmen in gold mines in Borneo, or in the United States. Chinese workers constructed railways in the USA and Panama. They went to South Africa, Cuba, Australia and Canada. In the USA, they rarely managed to break free of their employers to whom they were indebted. Japan also supplied indentured labour to the USA and Hawaii. The last place to abolish its indentured labour system was the Dutch colonies in 1941.

India was another major supplier of indentured labour. Indian workers went to the sugar plantations of Mauritius, the Caribbean, Africa, Burma and Malaysia. In 1856, the average death rate for Indians travelling to the Caribbean was 17 per cent. Once at work they were often treated like slaves, even inhabiting quarters vacated by slaves. Wages were low and conditions harsh. Many died. Those who survived had a chance to go home. Of 30 million Indians who became indentured labourers during one period, 24 million eventually returned to India. In the Pacific region, between 1840–1915, 280 000 Melanesians and Micronesians were exported as contract labour to Australia, Fiji, Papua New Guinea and other Pacific islands. The number of men, women and children involved was probably between 12 million and 37 million; nobody really knows.

Both slavery and indentured labour laid some significant seeds for today's legacy of poverty.

Links between poverty, migration and the demographic transition

The total population of industrialised countries is expected to grow slightly from 1.2 billion people in 1990 to 1.35 billion in 2025, but the population of developing countries is expected to have risen from 4 billion to 7.5 billion (Stalker 1994). In industrialised countries a *demographic transition* has taken place. In these countries, high birth rates were once cancelled out by high death rates, then better living standards and health care enable more children to survive. Death rates fell and the population expanded. Parents, on seeing more children survive, wanted a higher standard of living and reduced family size, resulting in roughly equal birth and death rates.

Such a transition may not occur in the same way in developing countries. For example, better living standards and health care may take a long time to arrive. Also, some developing countries have adopted rigorous family planning, with resulting lower birth rates. One key factor which may effect such a demographic transition, is whether the majority of the population gets access to productive employment and wage labour. This has both demographic and health effects.

2.10 UNEMPLOYMENT, UNDEREMPLOYMENT AND SOME HEALTH EFFECTS

In 1987, it was reported that some 500 million people globally were unemployed or underemployed. For poor households who survive on seasonal employment, such as harvesting bananas, sugar cane and coffee, the long 'lean' periods between one period of employment and the next constitute times of special risk to health and wellbeing. The unemployed spend less money on food and often do not have a balanced diet. Unemployment causes stress on personal and social relationships, which can eventually undermine psychological and emotional health. There is little or no money for medical treatment. In developing countries, there have been few studies of the health effects of unemployment, but evidence from industrialised countries indicates higher ill health and health-damaging habits, such as smoking, drug taking, consumption of alcohol and neglect of family planning.

2.11 STRANGERS IN THEIR OWN LAND – INDIGENOUS PEOPLES

Among the poorest and most vulnerable in some countries are the indigenous population. The rights of indigenous peoples to their land, natural resources and lifestyles have been continually eroded, whether from Spanish *conquistadores* (conquerors) in the Americas or today's multinational corporations and commercial enterprises. Even where governments contain wide-ranging and apparently clear guarantees for the rights of indigenous peoples, they appear blind to constant violation of such guarantees.

From Experience

The 9000 Yanomami people in Amazonas, Brazil, have lived in their forests for centuries. They move on, transferring their thatched communal houses, every three to four years from areas which they use, to allow soil, flora and fauna to regenerate. They 'walk' leaving the lightest of 'ecological footprints'. But their survival is threatened by the continuing invasion of mineral prospectors (around 100 000 by 1988) looking for uranium, casserite and gold, and those who extract timber. A road-building project through their territory seriously affected them with previously unknown diseases like smallpox, tuberculosis and sexually transmitted diseases, brought by the deforestation teams. They continue to be poisoned by consuming water contaminated by mining.

The official protection agency failed to move prospectors from the area in 1987. Some Yanomami were brutally murdered by gold prospectors. Their houses and gardens were destroyed. By 1989, Yanomami territory had been reduced by 70 per cent and the other 30 per cent divided into 19 discontinuous areas.

MAIN HEALTH EFFECTS OF POVERTY

This chapter looks first at the ways in which poverty and deprivation of basic needs, such as food, shelter, water, and sanitation affect health. Then it looks more deeply at how these factors and others affect health at various stages during a human life cycle. There are examples of preventive or remedial action, and diagrams to use and adapt. Finally the focus is on some diseases and conditions of ill-health which hit the poor hardest, like malaria, tuberculosis, intestinal helminths (worms), and mental disorders.

3.1 GETTING ENOUGH FOOD TO SUSTAIN LIFE AND HEALTH

Food has three important functions for the human body. It provides energy for all types of activity, helps the body grow in size and protects the body from disease. Different foods have different functions; they contain chemical substances known as *nutrients*. Commonly eaten foods can be divided generally into into three groups:

1 **Energy-giving foods:**
   Cereals like rice, wheat, corn, millet.
   Fats/oils like cooking oil.
   Starchy vegetables like sweet potatoes, potatoes, cassava.
   Sugar, molasses, honey.

2 **Growth-promoting foods:**
   Most foods of animal origin e.g. eggs, milk, fish, meat.
   Some foods of vegetable origin e.g. pulses, beans, peas, nuts.

3 **Protective foods:**
   Vegetables especially green leafy type.

Yellow/orange coloured fruits/vegetables e.g. carrots, papaya, pumpkin, mango, tomato, orange.

Fruits with sour juice e.g. lemon, lime, grapefruit, orange.

The human body has a minimal calorific daily requirement; around 3000 calories, depending on various factors. For example, an office worker will need less calories than a woman farmer weeding fields. But if the woman farmer is breastfeeding or pregnant, she will need even more calories, besides other types of *micronutrients* (very small amounts of substances essential for normal body functioning, such as breathing, circulation of blood). To maintain life and health the human body needs a mixture of foods which can provide energy, promote growth (and repair of the body) and protect from disease.

In developing countries, the majority of the poor and vulnerable groups live largely on diets consisting of cereals, beans and pulses, with some vegetables, cooking oil and fat. Items like meat, fish, milk and even eggs are rare. In principle, the diet of the poor is likely to be more healthy than that of the rich, who tend to over-consume foods of animal origin, fats and processed foods. The problem for the poor is that their diet is too often inadequate in size and irregular (depending on changes in season, whether they have land, their purchasing power or access to fuel). They simply do not get enough food. However, poor people who can eat a double mix of two or more vegetable foods, like beans and pulses (nuts are often expensive/sold as cash crops), or a triple mix of cereals plus pulses plus green leafy vegetables, from a nutritional perspective, are eating protein almost of the same quality as animal protein. However some of the poor, such as pregnant women and young children are particularly vulnerable to dietary deficiencies.

Foods needed by pregnant women who are poor

During pregnancy a woman's body grows very rapidly. Growth takes place inside her uterus (womb) as well as in her own body. In the course of only 280 days of pregnancy, a tiny fertilised egg cell grows into a fully formed baby of 2500 grams or more. The raw material needed for this tremendous growth is supposed to come from the diet of the mother. If the woman lives on a poor diet during pregnancy, her newborn baby will probably be lighter and smaller (a low birthweight baby). Such babies are more vulnerable, not only to nutritional deficiencies but also to infectious diseases.

Foods needed by young children who are poor

Breast milk is without equal in promoting growth of infants and very young children when given in addition to vegetable food mixture. Poor women should continue breastfeeding as long as possible. Infants and young children grow rapidly. A healthy newborn baby is supposed to double his/her weight in five months, as a result of increase in the amount of soft tissue (muscle, skin) and in the size of the bones.

Young children need growth-promoting foods, such as proteins to promote growth of soft tissues and minerals to promote the growth of bones. Foods for young children should contain pulses (such as lentils or gram) peas and beans, nuts, vegetables – especially the green leafy kind – milk and milk products, and some animal origin foods like fish and eggs. For the very poor this is usually not possible.

Infants and young children need plenty of energy-giving foods as they are usually very active. They need liquid or semi-liquid foods, or soft foods like cooked cereals, pulses, boiled mashed potatoes and less fibrous vegetables, with a little added oil or fat. Infants and young children have small stomachs and need small, more frequent feeding. Sadly, it is common in poor areas to see the right foods available, but not being prepared in a manner or amount to promote growth of poor children or protect them from disease.

Malnutrition and inadequate growth among young children is still widespread in developing countries. Main causes include declining breastfeeding practices, inadequate complementary feeding and weaning practices, and high infection rates. A study in an urban squatter area found that iron and vitamin A were estimated to be below what was needed in infants not receiving breast milk (Dorea & Furumoto 1992). A nutrition and health survey in a squatter area near Cape Town, South Africa, found that of 317 pre-school children, almost a quarter were stunted, indicating a chronic problem of undernutrition. In that area, three-quarters of the men and one-third of the women were unemployed. More than one in five households had no wage earners. Of 172 children under six years, 6.9 per cent had low birthweights. Half of these were underweight for their age, half were stunted, and a third were both underweight and stunted. Of the 4.2 per cent pre-school children being treated for tuberculosis, or who had completed treatment, 60 per cent were underweight, showing the link between tuberculosis and malnourishment (Le Roux & Le Roux 1991).

Eight factors which influence how much food a poor person gets, and some health effects

Some of these influencing factors relate to root causes of poverty, and some to environmental conditions and cultural patterns.

1 Access to land and means of food production

- No land, or insufficient arable land on which to grow food.
- Lack of money or credit to purchase agricultural tools, fertiliser and pesticides.
- Traditional agricultural methods phased out/forgotten.
- Water shortages, or the sources are owned by somebody else.
- Marketing systems not developed for food crops, livestock and cash crops.

2 Food crops versus cash crops

- Diet may be permanently deficient if production emphasis is on cash crops such as coffee and tobacco.
- The poor may not be able to eat some food crops or livestock as they need to sell them.

3 Dietary deficiencies due to seasonality and natural hazards

- Dietary deficiencies during gaps between harvests or end of the dry season.
- Deficiencies due to lack of vitamins in stored foodstuffs, and the fact that the best foodstuffs tend to get eaten first.

- Drought and other weather conditions interfere with food production.
- Food prices become inflated.

4 Preferences for 'modern' dietary patterns

- Dietary deficiencies resulting from habits or prejudices, such as preferring polished rice which is weak in vitamin B1.
- Fishermen throw away vitamin-rich fish livers.
- Preference for tinned food rather than fresh.
- Attractively packaged and promoted junk foods cause havoc to the diets of young children.

5 Expense of animal protein as a food

- Foods like meat, beef, pork and poultry are seen as luxuries, out of the reach of the poor.
- Cultural patterns and media influences conspire to make the poor want such products.
- The urban poor abandon their healthier, largely vegetarian, diet.
- Animal protein is expensive as a food.
- Animals tend to consume too many scarce resources for what they yield. For example, milk returns 15 per cent of the energy consumed, but in Asia, pigs eat edible garbage and can give a 20 per cent return on energy consumed.

6 Household expenditure on food

- A Guatemalan study of 200 low-income urban families found expenditure on food only increased slightly with improved income.
- Foods of animal origin plus rice, bread and flour are often were more popular than the traditional diet of beans, maize and root vegetables.
- In Mexico the urban poor are prone to fast foods, and these increase the risk of diabetes, particularly among the very poor (Quibrera Infante *et al.* 1994).

7 Capacity of the sick child to absorb food is undermined

- With a poor diet, poor children tend to get sick more easily.
- Malnutrition weakens the body's defences, so infections are worse and last longer.
- When poor children get sick, they cannot properly absorb the nutrients in the food they do get. This induces the circle of infection and malnutrition.
- Infections also cause poor appetite and use up stores of body nutrients.
- Local traditions and taboos may prohibit potentially nourishing foods, such as eggs, to sick children.

8 Allocation of food within a household

- In many societies men eat first, often leaving little for the women and children.
- In India, Africa and Mexico, women may eat at a different table/eating place from men.
- Young children may eat alone by the hearth.

- A study in Nepal found that young women were less likely to receive the same amount of food as men the same age, but during pregnancy and lactation they receive special foods.

3.2 SHELTER AND HEALTH OF THE POOR

Shelter, a place providing protection and safety, is an internationally recognised basic human need. To be adequate, shelter needs to be permanent, and those it protects must have security of tenure. But the shelter of the poor is often neither safe nor secure. It may be prone to flooding, fires or landslides where the subsiding earth descends, carrying with it the meagre shelter and belongings of the poor. There are also the 'clean-up' tactics of local authorities.

From Experience

In Nairobi, Africa, slum dwellers watch as their homes disappear in a cloud of debris and dust. Researchers in Bombay found that the average slum dweller had been forced to move home no less than five times because of official demolition programmes.

Impoverished rural people often drift into town looking for a better life. But finding adequate shelter is difficult. The poor erect shanty towns, creating basic shelter from whatever they can afford or scavenge, such as old wooden planks, corrugated iron sheets, cardboard boxes, plastic sheets and old blankets. The dwellings are unsteady monuments to human ingenuity – and desperation. They are small and cramped, and often dark – windows cost money, and can increase insecurity. The floor is often earthen. Cooking is done outside. Water may be drawn from a river, rarely from a public standpipe. Safe sanitation is non-existent. This type of 'shelter' is what the poor can afford. There is not much else to make life comfortable; or is there? In the slums of Dhaka, Bangladesh, a poor family may hang an electric bulb across a wall, scrape together money to buy little wooden stools for guests to sit on and adorn the walls with pictures of Indian film stars.

Safe, affordable and secure – the distant dream of pavement dwellers

Pavement dwellers face even harder struggles for survival. In India they have been described as 'the wretched of the city', existing a notch lower down the social scale than even the despised slum dwellers. Unlike the slums which, however derelict, have the potential to be 'regularised' and 'improved' by the authorities, pavement dwellers are often regarded as only an eyesore and nuisance to pedestrians. The pavement dwellers, often migrants from poor rural areas, may have been pushed off their plots because of environmental degradation or drought.

From Experience

In Bombay, the Society for Promotion of Area Resource Centres (SPARC) carried out a participatory survey with pavement women. It revealed that 6000 households lived on the pavements in just one area. A quarter of the pavement dwellers earned the equivalent of 50–86 US cents a day mostly as unskilled labourers, petty vendors of vegetables and domestic workers in middle-class families. Pavement dwelling had been viewed as temporary, but too often it had became permanent. SPARC helped the women themselves to be 'urban planners', working out who would be relocated to better housing. A 'family' had to be interpreted as a varying number of family members inhabiting the dwelling at different times of day and night, according to their work.

The women participated in a workshop to design their new homes. A public exhibition demonstrated full-size models of four types of home made of tin sheeting and sacking, and costing between US$422–930 equivalent. Top officials visited the exhibition. SPARC also helped women set up a savings scheme with a bank account, to help with their own housing fund.

Can policies and loans help the poor get housing?

In South Africa, housing organisations and governments have a system of conditional housing rights, to be received over time. Housing policy is to be implemented at local level. Quotas have been established for women, but more women's associations are required to enable women to participate in this development. In Mauritius, there is a housing savings bank account for anyone who can afford it, but the traditional and indigenous populations are left out. In Gambia, West Africa, a housing corporation has been established to make loans to middle and lower class people in urban areas. In Antigua, an island country in the Caribbean, lumber and house-building supplies are bought in bulk and stored for use. Low-income earners get loans and there is a high repayment rate.

Who among the poor is most at risk to health hazards from inadequate shelter?

Women and children are more likely to be exposed to domestic health hazards as they spend more time at home and their activities involve greature exposure to safety deficiencies and health hazards. **People living in sub-standard housing** or refugee settlements are exposed to special health risks from inadequacy of dwellings that are flimsy and makeshift, with no safe drinking water or excreta disposal, inadequate drainage or garbage disposal, overcrowding and vectors for disease such as house rats and insects. They often eat spoiled and undercooked food. They breathe air polluted by effluents of nearby industry, domestic cooking or heating. **Displaced and mobile populations,** such as refugees from war and civil disturbances, are also at risk, as are those uprooted by large-scale developments like dams or irrigation projects, and migrant labour families and nomadic populations. **Older people who are poor** are prone to extremes of cold, inadequate roofing, lack of warm clothes/blankets and lack of protection against rodents/ insects. Last are the **poor who have physical or mental disabilities** and cannot cope with extremes of heat or cold or undue noise, have inadequate protection against rodents and insects, and lack safe water, sanitation, security and special equipment.

Links between poverty, poor shelter and housing, and ill health

Overcrowding encourages the spread of diseases like measles and tuberculosis, both easily transmitted through person-to-person contacts.

Siting and drainage can cause health problems. For example, newly developing shanty town areas may spring up in areas liable to flooding (see water-related diseases later in this chapter). Construction materials can also contribute to health problems. For example, in northeast Brazil, the very poor live in dwellings with unplastered wooden houses, infested with the disease-causing Chagas beetles. Lack of cooking smoke exits also causes respiratory and eye problems.

Shelter and housing needed for good health

The table on page 43 sets out what type of shelter and housing the poor need if they are to maintain good health and prevent ill health. It is adapted from a table by Stephens *et al.* (1985).

Two of the most fundamental determinants of health and disease among people who are poor and vulnerable are access to safe drinking water and safe disposal of human excreta.

3.3 LACK OF CLEAN WATER AND SANITATION DAMAGES HEALTH

The body requires a constant supply of fresh water to function. Water is the main component of the body, accounting for two-thirds of its weight. Without water, nutrients and other necessary substances cannot be transported to body cells. Blood is mainly water and the whole circulatory system with its arteries and blood vessels is like a waterway along which nourishment is carried to its destination, and waste collected for excretion. Excretion itself requires water for the formation of stool and urine. Dehydration does not normally happen because the human thirst mechanism in the brain tells the body when it needs water. When dehydration is in its advanced stages, the person does not even feel thirst.

The poor are less likely to have clean water or sanitation

In 1995 it was reported that in 34 of the 47 least-developed countries (for the period 1988–91), only 46 per cent of the total population had access to safe water. Also, for 33 countries only 42 per cent of the rural population had access to safe water. In 30 countries, only 35 per cent of the total population had access to adequate sanitation, falling to 28 per cent in rural areas. This means that in the early nineties, less than half the total population in around 34 least-developed countries had safe water – and it fell to only one person in four in rural areas.

The struggle to provide safe water and what it costs

During the International Drinking Water Supply and Sanitation Decade of the 1980s, safe water supplies expanded. But the 1990s have seen budget cuts, increase in price of commodities (for water and sanitation installation, such as pump parts and cement slabs), over-consumption of water, pollution, and rising threats to water and sanitation from droughts and floods. Overall, progress in reaching the unserved has been poor since 1990.

Design features	Types of diseases combated

The big eight – strong association with ill health

1 Adequate and safe water supply.	Trachoma, skin infections, diarrhoeal diseases, cholera, typhoid.
2 Sanitary excreta disposal.	Intestinal parasites (worms), diarrhoeal diseases, cholera, typhoid.
3 Bathing and washing facilities (personal and domestic hygiene).	Skin diseases, schistosomiasis, trachoma, diarrhoeal diseases.
4 Means of food production.	Malnutrition, dietary deficiencies, anaemia.
5 Safe food preparation.	Diarrhoeal diseases, typhoid.
6 Control of air pollution.	Acute/chronic respiratory diseases.
7 Safe solid waste disposal.	Diarrhoeal diseases, cholera.
8 Plastered walls (e.g. mud-brick/plastered, not wood/woven).	Chagas disease (caused by beetle).

The next seven – fairly strong association with ill health

1 Poor ventilation and/or smoke from stove/fire; indoor air pollution.	Acute/chronic respiratory diseases, eye conditions.
2 Control of house dust.	Asthma.
3 Siting of shelter away from vector breeding areas (like stagnant water).	Malaria, schistosomiasis, filariasis, dengue fever, trypanosomiasis.
4 Control of open fires plus protection of kerosene and bottled gas.	Burns.
5 Finished floors (not earthen).	Hookworm.
6 Screening of windows and doors.	Malaria, filariasis, dengue fever, trypanosomiasis.
7 Drainage of surface water.	Malaria.

The last five – some association with ill health

1 Use of thatch material.	Chagas disease.
2 Rehabilitated housing.	Psychological disorders.
3 Control of heat inside shelter.	Heat stress.
4 Adequate food storage.	Malnutrition and deficiency diseases.
5 Refuse collection.	Chagas disease, leishmaniasis.

Approximately 1400 million people in the world still lack safe water, and perhaps 1900 million do not have adequate excreta disposal facilities. Rapid population growth and slow coverage expansion has left more people without access to safe water and sanitation today than in 1990. It is estimated to cost an average of US$105 per person to provide water supplies in urban areas and US$50 in rural areas, while sanitation costs an average of US$145 in urban areas and US$30 in rural areas (WHO 1996c).

Water, the urban poor and unhygienic practices

Unplanned urbanisation has also contributed to inadequate water supplies. For example, in Dar Es Salaam, Tanzania, 47 per cent of the population was reported to have no piped water supply, either inside or immediately outside their houses. Hardest hit by lack of drinking water are inhabitants of the spontaneous slum settlements which develop on city outskirts. Such people often rely on streams, brooks and shallow wells for their daily water supply. Even where there is piped water, it is rarely adequate. For example, in Ibadan, Nigeria, the water taps may not run for a whole week.

Water availability influences hygienic practices. A study in a water-scarce shanty town in Lima, Peru, found that in only three per cent of 300 cases of fecal contamination had people washed their hands within 15 minutes of defecating, showing how effective this precaution is in preventing contamination. The mean 12-hour per capita amount of water and soap used by the families was low. More than 80 per cent of the water stored by these families had *fecal coliforms* (was contaminated). Yet knowledge of the importance of hand-washing and other hygienic practices was high (Gilman 1993).

Action to preserve fresh water and install water systems

A UNDP-supported approach involved women not only in planning and establishing safe water systems, but they were also trained in the techniques of how to maintain those sources. Previously this has been the task of men. Other approaches have linked water and sanitation activities with increased livestock raising and kitchen gardens. Waste water ponds have also been created to enable families/communities to raise fish for consumption and sale. Nevertheless, most people who are poor, and still without safe water, continue to suffer from ill health.

Water-related diseases hit the poor hardest

Every year more than five million people die from illnesses linked to unsafe drinking water, unclean domestic environments and improper excreta disposal (WHO 1996c). It is estimated that water-borne diseases kill 25 000 children globally every day. Water contaminated by human, chemical or industrial wastes can cause a variety of communicable diseases through ingestion or physical contact. These diseases are:

1   Diseases caused by ingestion of contaminated water. This is water contaminated by human or animal faeces or urine containing pathogenic

(disease-causing) bacteria or viruses. Diseases include cholera, typhoid, amoebic and bacillary dysentery and other diarrhoeal diseases.

2   Diseases caused by insect vectors which breed in water. These include dengue haemorrhagic fever, malaria, yellow fever (caused by mosquitos), onchocerciasis, and trypanosomiasis.

3   Diseases caused by poor personal hygiene and skin and eye contact with contaminated water. These include scabies, trachoma (which causes blindness), and flea, lice and tick-borne diseases.

4   Diseases caused by parasites found in organisms living in water. They include dracunculiasis (guinea worm), schistosomiasis (bilharzia) and other helminths (worms).

Diarrhoeal diseases particularly affect children under five years, with an average of 3.5 episodes of diarrhoea per child per year. The poorest children may have up to ten episodes. Guinea worm disease affects adults who farm in irrigated fields, children who swim in irrigation canals, streams and ponds, and women and girls who wash clothes and domestic utensils in rivers and similar water sources. Schistosomiasis is caused by an organism which spends part of its life cycle in a water snail and causes human illness after entering through the skin or mucous membranes. Babies who are exclusively breastfed, and for a longer time, are less exposed to water-related diseases. Generally, many of the water-borne and water-related diseases could be prevented through safe water and sanitation, and hygienic behaviour.

What water means to women and families who are poor

In many developing countries women carry heavy loads of water on their heads. This not only produces extreme fatigue, but can result in personal injury, arthritis and slipped discs. It can also contribute to miscarriage. Time spent by women in collecting water (which can sometimes be as long as six hours a day) may act as a barrier to education. Water carrying under normal circumstances can use up to 12 per cent of a woman's daytime energy. In dry or mountainous regions this may reach 25 per cent. Children's education may also be interrupted to enable them to collect water.

> Safe water and proper disposal of human excreta could reduce morbidity and mortality of some of these diseases by 20–80 per cent (WHO 1996b).

Water near or in a household can mean better domestic hygiene, easier washing of cooking/eating utensils and the possibility for growing vegetables and raising small livestock. Food products from such activities can enhance the family diet and increase family income.

Safe water is needed for safe childbirth. For example, water is needed to clean the mother's genital area before birth. Safe water is needed for giving drinks to the mother in labour to avoid her dehydration and exhaustion. During birth, to prevent infections for mother and newborn, the 'three cleans' are advocated – clean washed hands, clean fingernails and a clean covering for the cut end of the umbilical cord of the newborn. Water is also needed to boil cord-cutting instruments such as a used razor blade (a new one is best).

Sanitation – many problems but few solutions

Efforts have been under way for decades to help poor households install safe disposal methods for human excreta. Many designs for pit latrines have been developed, most using little or no water. Pit latrines and septic tanks may be installed for individual households. Public communal pit latrines may be constructed in urban slums. But in the majority of very poor areas it is still uncommon to see adequate sanitation. Nearby fields are strewn with dried or drying faeces, open sewers run between the narrow lanes of urban shanty towns, and both adults and children defecate in the few open spaces. This ultimately creates conditions favouring the spread of typhoid, dysentery and diarrhoeal diseases. Young barefoot children play in the dust of dried fecal matter. They get diarrhoea and hookworm (which gains access to the body through bare skin).

As well as undermining household health, lack of safe water and adequate sanitation become public health problems. For example, Latin America was struck by a cholera epidemic for the first time this century. The outbreak begun in Peru with almost a quarter of a million cases in six months. It soon spread to neigbouring countries. Twelve African countries also suffered serious outbreaks, often with case fatality rates between 10–12 per cent, ten times higher than those reported in the Americas (Martin 1995).

Measures to reduce water- and excreta-related diseases among the poor are designed to stop spread of disease-causing organisms and depend on how each disease is transmitted, whether through water, fecal matter, contaminated food or dirty hands. People who are poor and vulnerable need a combined approach that deals with water sanitation and hygenic practices. Just introducing one element is insufficient – and may waste the time, labour and resources of the poor. The exact ways in which unsafe water and fecal matter cause individual diseases needs to be clearly understood. From this understanding can be developed practical and appropriate options and behaviour in a particular place. For example, after defecating, hand washing is needed before cooking and breastfeeding. Very poor households often cannot afford shoes for their young children, so restricting fecal matter to a pit latrine can prevent the children getting hookworm from dried fecal matter left in the open. The value of newly installed safe water can be undermined if it is stored in dirty, uncovered domestic containers.

So far, this chapter has looked at ways in which lack of basic needs like food, shelter, safe water and adequate sanitation affect the health of the poor. The next sections look at the ways in which poverty affects the poor in relation to eight stages of their life cycle.

3.4 HOW POVERTY AFFECTS HEALTH DURING A HUMAN LIFE CYCLE

The illustrated details of the human life cycle highlight the reproductive health of the poor, which means health in relation to reproductive functions such as conception and pregnancy.

The human life cycle and health-related effects of poverty – at a glance

Stage 1 Pre-conception and conception

- Malnutrition in young girls may cause defect in bony birth canal.
- Female genital mutilation may complicate childbirth.
- Ignorance of human sexuality can cause unplanned early pregnancy.
- Risk of unsafe abortion.
- Untreated genital herpes infection may infect baby at time of birth.
- Conception during a period of severe deprivation may increase chances of perinatal mortality.

Stage 2 Pregnancy and early fetal growth

- Some infections such as German measles, or drugs in first 40 days may damage fetus.
- Poor nutrition/toxic substances in first 12 weeks may cause congenital abormalities.
- Poor diet and lack of rest in pregnancy means poor fetal growth and low newborn birthweight.
- Risk of tetanus for newborn if mother not immunised.
- Risk of premature delivery if mother has toxaemia, haemorrhage, severe infection, multiple pregnancy etc.

Stage 3 Birth and early infancy

- Poor standard of newborn care.
- Greater risk of newborn death/disability.
- Breastfeeding shortened by next pregnancy.
- Contaminated bottle feeding.
- No/incomplete immunisation risks early childhood diseases.
- Poor and late weaning foods.
- Insufficient food for growth protection against disease.
- Unstimulating early childhood environment.

Stage 4 Young childhood (up to five years)

- Girls may receive less food/care than boys.
- Incomplete immunisation risks measles/polio/TB etc.
- Unsafe drinking water causes cholera.
- Fecally contaminated environment causes diarrhoeal diseases and worms.
- Inadequate food delays growth and reduces protection from infection.

Stage 5 Childhood 6–14 years

- Inadequate food causes malnutrition and stunting.
- Worms delay growth and lower resistance to disease.
- Inadequate protection against malaria.
- Poor girls lacking schooling is associated with poorer nutrition, higher birth rates and infant mortality as parents.

Stage 6   Adolescents and young adults (15–24)

- Ignorance of human sexuality can result in unplanned early pregnancy.
- Little/no access to pregnancy prevention.
- Liable to unsafe abortion.
- Little access to treatment/advice on sexually transmitted diseases.
- Poorly protected against HIV/AIDS.
- At risk of alcoholism/habit-forming dangerous drugs, including tobacco.
- At risk of traffic accidents/death.
- At risk of injury/death from violence.

Stage 7   Adulthood (15–49 years)

- Little/no antenatal care.
- Untrained birth attenders.
- Little/no care after birth.
- Dangers of maternal death/disability.
- Infection of genital tract.
- Little/no access to birth planning/spacing.
- Late treating diseases, e.g. TB, cancers.
- Inadequate protection against local diseases, e.g. malaria, shistosomiasis.
- Poorly protected against HIV/AIDS.
- At risk of occupational injuries.

Stage 8   Older adulthood (50 and above)

- At risk of social isolation and extreme poverty.
- Higher risk of cancer of cervix from untreated genital warts.
- Undernutrition due to poor diet.

The human life cycle and health-related effects of poverty – in some detail

Stage 1 Pre-conception and conception

During the early stage of a woman's life, specific factors can influence both her physical health and that of her fetus when she becomes pregnant. For example, the practice of female genital mutilation (female circumcision) may cause complications during birth as a baby attempts to pass through a birth canal which has been scarred and narrowed at the outlet by such practices. Also, malnutrition in a young girl may have caused defects in the bony part of her birth canal. A young woman who is poor may not understand much about human sexuality and exactly how pregnancy takes place. This can cause unplanned early pregnancy and risks unsafe abortion. Women who are poor are often deprived of opportunities to plan and space their families. Generally, they become pregnant too early, too often and continue to get pregnant too late in their lives. A poor woman may be either pregnant or breastfeeding for around 18 years of her life. Conception during a period of severe deprivation may also increase chances of perinatal mortality.

During pregnancy, rapid growth takes place in both the body of the woman and the fertilised human egg cell which, during the average 280 days of pregnancy, grows into a fully formed baby of around 2600 grams. If the mother is poor, inadequately fed and works too hard, the baby will be lighter and smaller at birth, and more vulnerable to nutritional deficiencies and infectious diseases. Some infections (such as german measles) and some medicines, if taken during the first 40 days of pregnancy, may damage the growing fetus. Poor nutrition and toxic substances in the first 12 weeks of pregnancy may cause congenital abnormalities. There is a risk of tetanus for the newborn if the mother is not immunised. Also, if the mother has a severe infection, bleeding or toxaemia, the delivery may be premature (before 37 weeks), with attendant risks to the newborn.

If the pregnant woman suffers from malaria, the fetus can be prevented from getting normal nourishment from the mother's placenta. For this reason anti-malarials may be given routinely to pregnant women, along with iron and folic acid to prevent anaemia. However, without antenatal care women may not receive such inputs. There is some basic action they themselves can take through eating green leafy vegetables and avoiding malaria.

When pregnancy takes place in a young girl who is malnourished and not fully grown herself, there are particular dangers to her health and life, as well as to her child. She will stop growing. She is more likely to experience complications during pregnancy and childbirth, and could even die. In Ethiopia, the maternal mortality rate in the age group 15–19 years is three times higher than that in the age group 20–24 years. In northern Nigeria, in the absence of antenatal care, 5–7 per cent of pregnant girls under 17 may die. When such child-bearing children survive and are still fertile, they face the prospect of repeated complications during future childbearing.

In many places access to antenatal care has become more difficult for poor women. Reasons for this include cuts in budgets, introduction of user fees for health care and cuts in health staff production and employment. For example, in Senegal, West Africa, the output of professional health worker training establishments was reduced from 100 to 30 for state nurses and from 100 to 25 for midwives (Coll 1990). Neglect of antenatal care is directly related to complications of pregnancy and childbirth, and to the death or disability of mother and/or child. Around 600 000 women in developing countries die every year due to such largely preventable complications. The five main killers are:

- obstructed labour (baby cannot emerge from the birth canal, usually because the bony part of the mother's birth canal is small or distorted by disease)
- haemorrhage (heavy bleeding before, or usually after, childbirth)

- puerperal sepsis (infection beginning in the genital tract following delivery or abortion)
- hypertensive diseases of pregnancy (raised blood pressure and other symptoms including fits which eventually can kill mother and fetus)
- abortion (spontaneous or induced termination of pregnancy during the first 28 weeks).

The Safe Motherhood Initiative is striving to prevent and reduce maternal and newborn deaths

The global Safe Motherhood Initiative sponsored by the United Nations since 1987 continues to draw attention to practical ways in which maternal and newborn mortality can be prevented. But in many developing countries, particularly in rural and remote areas, health facilities still do not have the equipment and skills to handle common complications of pregnancy or childbirth. The locally trained Traditional Birth Attenders (TBAs) provide an important service, especially for the very poor, but they cannot be effective without regular supervision and referral services for complicated cases and emergencies. In some countries in Africa and Latin America, *maternity waiting homes* have been established close to a referral hospital (and to health centres in some places), where women with danger signs during pregnancy can wait in a safer place for their deliveries.

The life cycle of a female fetus may be short. For example, in India and China the desire for a son is almost obsessional, as it can provide parents with more security in old age; boys do not require a dowry (India) and the son carries on the family name. In both countries, vast numbers of female fetuses are being aborted, with 10 million official abortions carried out each year of which 97 per cent are female fetuses. In India sex-determination tests (using a scan) are illegal, but still the practice continues; people prefer to pay US$15 for a scan which could avoid the risk of having a girl child whose dowry might eventually cost US$1500 (Chester 1996). A study in rural north India found that the poor were using high fertility and female infanticide to maximise the number of male children to ensure family welfare (Wadley 1993).

Women who are poor often seek back-street abortions

Termination of unplanned and unwanted pregnancies is common in the lives – and too often the deaths – of women who are poor and vulnerable. They may get little or no opportunity to plan and space pregnancies. The poor desperately need such opportunities, without violating their own local cultural/spiritual beliefs and customs. Unless they are available, abortion, especially unsafe back-street abortion, will continue.

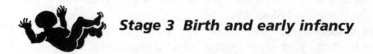 ***Stage 3 Birth and early infancy***

Eight out of ten women in developing countries still do not have trained assistance during childbirth. If there are complications, poor women bleed to death waiting at the roadside for passing transport to take them to a faraway hospital, or they just die at home. They are the ones who endure degrading lack of control over their urine (or faeces) because they suffered an untreated internal injury during childbirth. In Nepal, where the maternal mortality rate is 850/100 000 live births – meaning that more than eight in every thousand pregnant women die of pregnancy or birth-related complications (one of the highest maternal mortality rates in the world) – there is one doctor per 30 thousand people, and 90 per cent of births are not attended by a trained attendant (Bhattaria 1993).

Trained maternal and child health personnel, particularly midwives, are becoming scarcer in many developing countries, and where they do exist they may be concentrated in urban areas. Some senior nurses are leaving to take up more lucrative employment, especially in the private sector. Those who do practice are often under-equipped, unsupported and without in-service training or skills upgrading. Health facilities, such as district hospitals and larger health centres, which want to provide 'essential obstetric care' (as advocated by WHO) are still being handicapped by lack of resources and opportunities to upgrade equipment and skills.

Generally, standards of maternal and newborn care are still low for women who are poor. Care after birth is even more neglected than care before birth, thus opportunities are also lost for offering family planning and spacing opportunities, as women/couples are often more interested in such options during the postnatal period.

Hazards for newborn who are poor

When underweight mothers give birth to low birthweight (LBW) babies, the latter have poorer chances of survival, healthy growth and development than those with normal birthweights. Besides being more prone to illness and death, they tend also to experience greater mental, physical and neurological handicaps later in life.

The health of the newborn is largely determined by the mother's own health status and access to health care, but there is one asset that even a very poor newborn can have – breast milk. It is the ideal nutrient for the newborn; balanced, clean and free. In developing countries, the custom of breastfeeding is still widespread in many places among the poor. However, in order to produce enough breast milk of good quality, a mother must have a diet consisting of adequate amounts of cereals, pulses, beans, vegetables, oils and, if possible, animal foods. For women who are poor, having an adequate diet during lactation is often difficult.

Exclusive breastfeeding is best for newborn and young infants who are poor. Where newborn and young infants are not breastfed, or are partly breastfed, they may unwittingly be given a lethal mixture of contaminated bottle feeds that are unhygienically prepared and made up with unsafe water.

One of the causes of newborn morbidity and mortality is neonatal tetanus. A study in war-torn Angola of 199 infants with neonatal tetanus admitted to hospital over a five-month period resulted in an 80 per cent death rate. Almost all newborns were from families who had moved from rural areas into the urban slums of the capital. They lived under extremely poor and very unsanitary conditions. Of the births, 69 per cent had been home deliveries, 15 per cent were delivered by TBAs and 57 per cent of the mothers had not received antenatal care (during which immunisation against tetanus of the newborn is routinely given). Although 31 per cent of mothers had visited a health facility one or more times, they had received no immunisation against tetanus (Grudeboen 1987). Other health hazards for newborn and young infants who are poor include no, or inadequate, immunisation against preventable early childhood diseases, poor and late weaning foods, insufficient food for growth and protection against disease.

A newborn baby should weigh at least two and a half kilos. If it grows well, it should weigh about six kilograms at five months, and nine kilograms at one year. Healthy babies are supposed to double their birth-weights in five months, and treble them in 12 months. After that, the weight increase is slower, at around two kilograms per year. At birth a baby is around 50 cm long and by one year of age should be about 72 cm long. A baby's head grows very quickly because of rapid brain growth. Development, or increase of skills, mainly depends on development of the brain and nervous system which require adequate nutrition, just like other parts of the body. Adequate nutrition and early childhood stimulation will mainly determine how the young infant grows and develops. The infant who is poor often lacks both.

Stage 4 Young childhood (up to five years)

Many studies focus on only one aspect at a time of poverty in relation to health. In reality, many aspects of poverty converge at the same time to affect the health of the young child. A study in southwest Uganda revealed that lack of ownership of cattle, recent arrival in a village, using candles for lighting, being in a family of five or more, having a divorced mother or a father with less than eight years of schooling were significantly associated with child mortality, along with nutritional status (Vella *et al.* 1992).

Young children are particularly susceptible to the adverse effects of poverty. They face more frequent exposure to disease, pollution, toxic substances and family stress, as well as more consequences from such risks. In the Brazilian city of Fortaleza, a study revealed an association of malnutrition with increased diarrhoea incidence and duration among slum children. Overall, the most malnourished children had nearly twice the total number of days of diarrhoea than better nourished children (Schorling *et al.* 1990).

In the most impoverished communities, young children who survive repeated cycles of diarrhoeal and respiratory diseases or malnutrition fail to attain full adult growth. They may also fail to attain full psychosocial and mental development. If they suffered lack of oxygen during a poorly managed birth, they may have sustained some damage to the brain. This may not be apparent until the child enters school, if the child enters school at all. There may be visual or hearing defects or disordered learning or behavioural patterns. Undetected and uncorrected, many minimal disorders of sight, hearing or speech may have profound effects on the child's learning ability and school performance, on self esteem, general behaviour and subsequent personality.

Only integrated approaches can make any lasting impact on the health of the child up to five years of age. For example, if a poor household struggles to get water, this may not necessarily protect child health if the surrounding environment is itself poor, insanitary and detrimental to health. Studies in urban slum children in northeast Brazil found clear evidence that contamination by domestic animals causes diarrhoeal diseases (Newman *et al.* 1993). Promoting nutritional supplements may be helpful, but only in the short term. Promoting better weaning practices may also be helpful, but only if parents have access to the food and safe water concerned.

Being fully immunised against the six major preventable diseases of childhood (measles, polio, diphtheria, whooping cough, tetanus and tuberculosis) constitutes one of the potential few health assets of a young child who is poor. However, since 1991 immunisation coverage has fallen in many countries. This is especially true of poorest countries, where the impact of vaccine-preventable diseases is greatest. Of the 15 countries in Africa reporting data to the World Health Organization in 1991, and classified as least-developed countries, 13 reported a decline in coverage. This fall took place after a consistent rise in coverage between 1986–90. Such a decline particularly affects the most vulnerable mothers and infants (Poore 1993). Immunisation only works if the complete course of immunisation is taken correctly – and if the vaccines are potent. In some places, the *cold chain system* (of getting potent vaccines to their destinations) is breaking down, and much effort is required to ensure it continues to function effectively.

Poverty itself can create stress and frustrations which prevent parents from providing the kind of care they really desire for their children. Poor parents often feel depressed and powerless, violent due to anger (and sometimes alcohol or drug abuse), and disorganised due to feelings of alienation. Poverty can also undermine good emotional bonding within the family setting and extended family networks. Poverty makes some parents more likely to be violent towards their children.

> Parenting and caregiving are often undermined by poverty

But poverty does not always lead to such poor outcomes for young children. The situations of families who are poor vary widely. For example, where poor children get stimulation, parental support and attention to their safety, they may be more resilient to poverty than those who do not. Poor children who have a single risk factor such as unsafe water, but other assets, may fare better than those who had a low birth weight and have an unsupportive home as well as a contaminated environment, an alcoholic parent and a learning disability. It is when multiple deprivation and effects of poverty converge that effects can be most damaging. There is also a greater likelihood of mental disorder.

Stage 5 Childhood (6–14 years)

For poor children between 6 to 14 years of age who have not been, or were inadequately, immunised common health problems include skin diseases and conditions (like scabies), and infections and communicable diseases. Inadequate food intake causes malnutrition and stunting of normal growth. Poor children of school-age frequently have intestinal worms, which absorb the nutrients ingested, thus depriving the growing child. Poor children who go to school may often be absent from school due to ill health, for example with malaria. Children who go to school may receive some family life education on human sexuality, and on prevention against HIV infection and AIDS. Children who drop out of primary school – or who never enter it in the first place – are often at particular risk to early marriage and early pregnancy, as well as sexually transmitted diseases including HIV infection. Some children of school age are also members of the workforce, engaged in herding livestock, or in low-paid employment, with few if any occupational health safeguards.

Approaches to reach children who go to school and those who do not include the child-to-child approach, which links the school with the home and the community. The regular – but often decreasing – school health checks organised by public health services, fulfil an important function for poor children, giving them access to immunisation, growth monitoring and treatment of common diseases and conditions.

Stage 6 Adolescents and young adults (15–24 years)

Adolescence has been defined as being between the ages 10–19 years and youth is between 15–24 years (WHO). Adolescence and youth is a period of transition from childhood to adulthood, marked by changes in the body, mind and social relationships. While the sequence of changes tends to be the same for all, how long the changes last and their outcomes are influenced by gender, culture and individual personalities and circumstances. In many societies, the conditions in which young people now live have changed radically from those of their parents, and they have to face changes within themselves at the same time as changes in the world about them. Whether such changes will occur in a healthy way depends on factors like the home, community, school, work and leisure. Many poor young people in developing countries are deprived of basic needs like adequate nutrition, safe water and sanitation, educational and employment opportunities, and secure and loving family relationships. They are attracted to dangerous substances such as tobacco, alcohol and other drugs. They are also affected by dangerous conditions on the road, in the workplace, or by conflict and war. These factors, plus instability in the family often combine to cause health-damaging behaviour.

The health of young people is influenced by nutrition and care during childhood, and whether serious and debilitating infections and illnesses occurred. Serious childhood infections, such as tuberculosis or rheumatic heart disease are often exacerbated during adolescence. If immunisations have not been effective, or natural immunity acquired during childhood, adolescents can get infections such as poliomyelitis and mumps with possible paralysis and infertility. The combination of the energy demands of the adolescent growth spurt and an inadequate diet may contribute to tuberculosis. Adolescent girls are said to require 10 per cent more iron than boys to make up for the losses in menstrual blood.

Generally, adolescents are prone to poor eating habits with consequent nutritional deficiencies. They often neglect care of their teeth and oral hygiene. It is often a time of irresponsible sexual relationships leading to unwanted pregnancies, the dangers of unsafe abortion and sexually-transmitted diseases, including HIV infection. In some countries suicide among adolescents, violence to oneself or others, and mental breakdown are factors connected to adolescent deprivation. Trauma, particularly violence, is increasing in cities like Sao Paulo in Brazil, Lusaka in Zambia and Manila in the Philippines. For example, violence (mostly homicides) accounts for 86 per cent of all deaths in boys 15–19 years old in Sao Paulo, and over half the deaths in 5–14 year olds (Stephens *et al.* 1994).

Occupational health for adolescents and young people – a neglected area

A disproportionate number of urban migrants are young (about a quarter are between 15–24), usually seeking education or employment. Young migrants often encounter new cultural patterns and frequently a hostile environment. This they may have to face without parental support, and it may lead to an increase in their mental and behavioral problems. Among those most vulnerable are homeless youths, refugees and victims of war. Many adolescents and young people start their working life too early and are either unable to go to school, or they work and go to school at the same time. They suffer from fatigue and a higher accident rate than adult workers.

Estimates suggest that there are around 80 million young workers between the ages of 10–14 in the world, primarily in developing countries. It is hard to get the true figures as the employment is often hidden and underpaid. Few countries possess reliable statistics on young workers. The work place and tools of work are almost always designed for adults. The incompletely grown adolescent in such circumstances works inefficiently, is less experienced in the handling of tools and machines, and more liable to occupational linked injury or death. (WHO 1989).

Special needs of street children and young people

In many urban areas of the developing world there are large numbers of children, adolescents and young people working and/or living on the streets. They are at particular risk from taking addictive substances and from unprotected sexual activity. Heavy substance abuse may be linked to neurological deficits. Other negative outcomes include premature pregnancy, sexually transmitted diseases including HIV/AIDS. Street children/adolescents also risk injury and death. Of 119 street children involved in an 18 month study in Brazil, six died during the study (Campos *et al.* 1994).

The daily life of street youths is made even more difficult by the inefficiency or lack of public services that are intended to satisfy their basic social rights. The only public authority which seems to reach them is the police. Teams of street educators have been set up in some places to reach street youths. These outreach workers bridge the gap between street youth and health services and professionals.

A Brazilian study found that poor 9–18 year olds who lived at home and worked on the streets appeared to be experiencing orderly development, but those who both worked and lived on the street showed signs of psychological and physical risk due to parental loss, diminished social support, drug abuse and early onset of sexual activity. What happens to many street children when they grow up is largely unknown – but thought to be grim (Campos *et al.* 1994). In 1991, of Sao Paulo's prison population, 80 per cent had formerly been street children, but some positive action has taken place elsewhere in Brazil. For example, AXE is an organisation to help street youth. It runs children's theatre, paper recycling and metal workshops, a circus school and literacy classes. It has enabled more than 3000 children to leave the street and by 1993, 1700 of those children had found jobs or were back home and in school. The country's largest construction firm offers placements to AXE's former street children. AXE itself offers children three meals a day, scholarship money, a bus travel card, and about a third of the minimum salary of about US$10 equivalent a month. Two Italian dress designers got involved, and helped set up two fashion boutiques with clothes designed and made by the children under the designers' supervision.

Stage 7 Adulthood (15–49 years)

For people who are poor, adulthood may begin while the person is still biologically not yet out of childhood. For example, where there is still child marriage, the girl may become pregnant about three years before full growth. For adults, reproductive health needs and problems exert a dominant influence during this long stage of the life cycle. For a minority the problem may also be infertility, perhaps caused by sexually transmitted diseases. Little in the way of counselling and treatment of fertility may be available. Cancers of the female reproductive tract tend to be diagnosed late, as few early detection services are available to the poor. In developing countries, reproductive and sexual health problems account for over a third of the total burden of disease in women, compared with about 10 per cent for men. Reproductive health is affected by many factors such as socio–economic circumstances, education, shelter, employment and health service access.

Access to pregnancy planning and spacing often determines the level of poverty and health of the poor adult and of their family. Uncontrolled and unwanted pregnancies can entangle them in a seemingly endless web of deprivation, reducing their chance of breaking out of the cycle of poverty. Women also need care for the periods between pregnancies. Poor women find it harder to obtain early diagnosis for diseases such as tuberculosis or cancers, and may only seek care at a late stage – if at all. They are often poorly protected from HIV infection, for example from infection through husband or partner with multiple sex partners. They are also liable to hazards and injuries from low-paid work. Adult (and adolescent) women usually bear the brunt of family health problems. They become the first – and often the only – resource to remedy insufficiencies in official health systems, but their abilities are determined by their own physical condition, knowledge and economic status.

The adult male who is poor may risk diseases and conditions such as alcoholism and tobacco abuse (often spending the family's food money). Male poverty is often associated with violence, especially in urban areas or in situations of social injustice and conflict. It is more often men than women who are carried into health facilities with cuts from machetes, stabs or gunshot wounds. Links between occupation and health are strong and the unsafe workplace presents dangers to health. For example, the farmer who labours in forests may catch malaria, or the miner tunnelling underground might develop a chronic respiratory condition. Something which causes mild symptoms now could have serious long-term effects. The information provided on p. 58 shows types of health problems that an unsafe workplace can cause.

Bodily harm in the workplace

Something that causes mild symptoms now could have serious long term effects. Don't ignore headaches, frequent colds and coughs, dizziness or skin irritation. Symptoms may be caused by poor working conditions or chemicals.

Stage 8 Older adulthood (50 and above)

For many older persons who are poor, health care is not easy to access. It may be too far away or too expensive. Often, treatable conditions are not cured or even alleviated. For example, cataracts (cloudiness of the usually clear lens or covering of the eye) may be regarded as normal. The health of older persons is also influenced by social factors, such as the breakdown of extended family and insecurity regarding status. They may lose access to food, ownership of property and all sources of economic and social power; they may end up as beggars in their own homes, their vulnerability to anorexia and malnutrition further compounded by depression, disorientation and isolation (Marlow 1993).

Malnutrition among older people is often linked to poverty, though little is known about the magnitude and gravity of malnutrition among older people in developing countries. Conflicts and disasters can create particularly acute situations for older people, whether it is malnutrition in times of famine or drought, or distress and depression as refugees. Generally, attention is focused on childhood malnutrition, but older people who need

EYES **Symptoms**: redness, irritation, watery, grainy feeling, 'welder's flash', actinic conjunctivitis, blindness. **Common causes**: smoke, eye strain, mechanic trauma, gases, (ozone), fumes (ammonia), metal dust, acids, ultraviolet radiation.

NOSE and THROAT **Symptoms**: sneezing, coughing, sore throat. **Common causes**: caustic soda, wool/cotton dust, hardwood dusts and resins, dynes.

CHEST and LUNGS **Symptoms**: wheezing, congestion, dry cough, shortness of breath after mild exercise, flu-like symptoms (metal fume fever). **Common causes**: organic dust (e.g. cotton/textile dust, detergent, enzymes, animal products, moulds), dust (e.g. asbestos), metal oxides from welding.

LIVER **Symptoms**: disturbed liver function, liver cancer. **Common causes**: polychlorinated dibenzofurans, dibenzdioxins, hexachlorobenzene, methylene diamine, vinylchloride.

BONES **Symptoms**: arthritis (early). **Common causes**: excessive vibration, constant dampness, physical overload.

HEAD **Symptoms**: Dizziness, headache, drowsiness. **Common causes**: solvents, ozone, heat exhaustion, noise, eye strain.

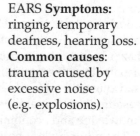

EARS **Symptoms**: ringing, temporary deafness, hearing loss. **Common causes**: trauma caused by excessive noise (e.g. explosions).

TEETH and GUMS **Symptoms**: corrosion of tooth enamel, blue gums. **Common causes**: acid fumes, cellulose, acetate production, lead poisoning.

MUSCLES and BACK **Symptoms**: soreness, strain. **Common causes**: excessive or improper lifting, bending, vibration, poorly designed chairs, heavy carrying loads, psychological strain.

ARM and HAND **Symptoms**: pain, swelling, numbness tingling, cuts, loss of fingers/hand/arm, 'white fingers'. **Common causes**: rapid repetitive movement, vibration, dangerous machinery.

KIDNEYS **Symptoms**: disturbed kidney function. **Common causes**: heavy metals (lead, mercury, cadminum).

BLADDER **Symptoms**: cancer. **Common causes**: benzidine, betanaphtylamine.

NERVOUS SYSTEM: **Symptoms**: stress, nervousness, irritability, sleeplessness, tremors, heart palpitations, anxiety, depression, fatigue, emotional instability, poor concentration, memory disturbance, hypertension, gastric ulcer. **Common causes**: piece work rates, noise, metal poisoning (lead, mercury), sexual harassment, shift work, exploitation, lack of job control, solvents, pesticides.

SKIN **Symptoms**: redness, dryness, itching, ulcers, skin cancer. **Common causes**: solvents epoxies, oil, fibre glass, caustic soda, nickle, mineral oils, pitch, arsenic, tar, radiation, chromium, dyes, detergents, cement.

REPRODUCTIVE SYSTEM: **Symptoms**: miscarriage, menstrual irregularities, anatomical or functional disturbances in the offspring, diminished fertility. **Common causes**: lead, pesticides, ionsing, radiation, anaestetic gas, polystryrene production, xylene, some solvents, benzene, mercury radiation.

Adapted with permission from AHRTAG UK

help to obtain food are also in danger of malnutrition. Elderly people may even be the first to suffer from malnutrition in times of food shortage, as they may deliberately reduce their own food intakes in favour of children. Ways of measuring malnutrition among older people are inadequate at present and alternative ways are being explored.

Many older people who are poor in developing countries have survived a lifetime of exposure to infections and parasites, and women have often had a lifetime of multiple pregnancies and chronic anaemia. Older people may have survived food shortages and chronic dietary insufficiencies. Health problems for older people may include skin infections, such as leprosy, infestations and ulcers. Some also face hearing impairment and increasing deafness. They are more likely than other age groups to suffer from stroke, cancer, coronary heart disease, diabetes and arthritis. Some are affected by chest infections such as chronic bronchitis and emphysema (gaseous over-distension of the lung), asthma, lung cancer and breathing difficulties. Others experience disorders of the heart and circulatory system, such as heart attacks, high blood pressure, arterial disease or gangrene. They may also experience joint pains due to rheumatism and rheumatoid arthritis. Common foot complaints include neglected foot sores and toenails. Common eye diseases and conditions include failing vision and blindness.

Older people must keep healthy to work and support their families

Most older people in developing countries need to remain healthy because they must continue working. They usually do not have pensions – or they have minute pensions insufficient for everyday needs.

Older women often serve as the economic and emotional mainstay of their families, serving as the nucleus around which the family is organised. They sustain and are sustained by it. They act as provider, arbiter, caregiver, disclipinarian, housekeeper, cook, repair person, sometimes family representative to the community and often main decision maker (Smyke 1991). The life of an elderly poor women is often arduous. Even when healthy, she may have difficulty in some tasks, such as fetching water and firewood. With multiple responsibilities and tasks, she can also suffer from anxiety, stress and depression.

AIDS and its burden on older people

HIV infection and AIDS affect elderly people in developing countries in various ways. For example, premature death of their sons and daughters often leaves widows/widowers and children to be cared for by the elderly. Although elderly and poor, they are called upon to provide education, food, clothing, shelter and medical care. This creates additional workloads and stress, for which elderly people are often ill prepared. Parents who have made many sacrifices to educate their children may have to watch them succumb to HIV infection and AIDS. In this way older people lose their heirs. The death of young men may leave behind young widows.

Involving older people in action for health and against poverty

For older women with family ties and responsibilities, an income can make a difference to the lives of the many people who often depend on them. In Haryana, India, older women in a drought-prone and poor area have joined an income-generating scheme through which they earn an income for themselves and pass on carpet weaving skills to other women. In Thailand, an up-country programme involves health education, nursing services and medical care made available to older people who themselves have established an informal care network, visiting club members too sick to attend the centre (Helpage International 1995).

In South Africa, the Muthande Society for the Aged (MUSA) developed from a feeding programme and operates in three poor urban areas in Natal province. It aims to meet older people's most basic needs and reach them in their own home. Home helps receive in-service training in weekly sessions over 18 months in between practical work. Topics include physiotherapy, nutrition, basic medication, alcohol abuse, incontinence and pressure sores.

Older people often suffer undue hardship in the already difficult conditions of the refugee camps. Often frail and having perhaps lost family members, with no family support or social welfare system their prospects are bleak. Generally, strategies for older refugees need to include advocacy (to ensure that older people's needs are met, for instance, so that they receive their fair share of rations), primary health care, education, income generation, shelter, therapeutic activities rehabilitation for older people with disabilities, provision of basic goods, family tracing, attention to water and sanitation, and seed and tool distribution.

3.5 CAUGHT IN AN EPIDEMIOLOGICAL TRAP?

When people move out of poverty the pattern of diseases which affect them usually changes from infectious diseases (like cholera, tuberculosis or measles) to chronic diseases (like heart conditions and cancers). This is called an *epidemiological transition*. It appears that in some places people who are poor, particularly in urban areas, are caught in an epidemiological trap where they still suffer and die from infectious diseases, but are also getting chronic diseases.

From the relatively few studies of poverty-related chronic disease in urban areas of developing countries, it appears that diseases of the heart (through diet, health behaviour and psycho–social factors) and neoplasms (tumours and growths) are emerging as significant urban health problems, along with chronic respiratory conditions in adults. For example, a study in Ghana, West Africa, showed that age-adjusted rates of mortality from heart disease were 2.3 times higher for the 43 per cent of the capital city's population in the worst zone than those for the residents of the most affluent zone (Stephens 1994). The poor often face the double burden of diseases from both infectious and non-communicable diseases.

3.6 DISEASES WHICH HIT THE POOR HARDEST

There are certain diseases which particularly affect poor and vulnerable groups, including malaria, leprosy, dracunculiasis (guinea worm), Chagas disease, schistosomiasis (bilharzia), trypanasomiasis (sleeping sickness), dengue, dengue haemorrhagic fever and intestinal helminths (worms). In order to look more closely at links between poverty and health, four of these diseases are now considered.

Malaria

This has plagued mankind for thousands of years. In 1992, it was reported to be causing a death every second in the world, with a total of 100 million annually falling ill from it, often severely. Around two million people a year die of malaria (WHO 1995b). Malaria threatens 40 per cent of the world's population; it debilitates the working population and undermines the health and welfare of women and families. It causes anaemia in children and pregnant women, and increases vulnerability to other diseases. Malaria is a main cause of school absenteeism.

Malaria is transmitted through the bite of a female anopheline mosquito, itself carrying the parasite which causes malaria. History shows that there is no single method of bringing the disease under control and it is in poorer countries that malaria has its greatest impact. In Africa 500 million people, mainly in tropical areas, live in areas lacking strong and effective anti-malaria efforts. Elsewhere in poorer countriers the disease has spread because of major ecological changes, such as economic exploitation of forest areas, social or political unrest and large-scale population move-ments with disruptions of established malaria programmes. For example, two-thirds of malaria cases in the Americas occur in the Amazonian basin as a result of colonisation and mining of the forest environment; poor fam-ilies move into an area, cut down the forest to grow food or cash crops. Malaria and poverty are closely linked.

In sub-Saharan Africa, 100 million clinical cases of malaria are reported every year, resulting in close to one million deaths. The problem is worse than it was a decade ago, yet little is being done beyond attempts to improve management of malaria cases when they occur. In many places, deteriorating health services contribute to this problem. Resources, money and political will are not there to tackle the underlying problems of pre-vention and control.

The search has been on to find new options for malaria control, such as use of the traditional Chinese anti-malaria drug, artemisinin. There is some evidence that it can be useful in treating malaria fevers and clearing para-sites from the bloodstream faster than any other anti-malarial drug. Elsewhere, mosquito nets are impregnated with the insecticide, perme-thrine, but in many countries people who are poor find it hard to afford mosquito nets. When they do have nets, there is often the problem of obtaining reimpregnation after six months. This reduces the ability of the poor to avoid malaria transmission.

Approaches which have worked in some places include use of primary community-based malaria workers who also provide basic presumptive treatment (in case it is malaria). Other schemes involve establishing revolving funds to enable families who are poor to purchase mosquito nets, permethrine, screening for windows and doors.

Chagas disease

This disease, common among the poor in some parts of the Americas, is spread by a particular beetle which inhabits the wood/woven structures of unplastered houses. The disease attacks tissues of the brain, heart, oesophagus (food pipe) and intestines, causing irreparable damage and eventually death. There is little information on Chagas-related deaths as most are attributed to cerebral haemorrhage, heart failure or intestinal blockages. Once the disease becomes chronic, it cannot be effectively treated. In Bolivia, South America, a community development approach was used to identify and kill the beetles in a low-income rural area. Houses were fumigated, house construction improved, and people educated on Chagas prevention (Renshaw & Rivas 1991).

Tuberculosis

It is estimated that tuberculosis (TB) killed some three million people in 1993 (WHO 1995b). Also in that year, it was estimated that there would be 8.8 million new cases of TB. That corresponded to 52 000 deaths weekly from TB, or 7000 daily. Some 80 per cent of those affected by TB are in the economically productive age group 15–49 years of age. TB is now the leading infectious killer of youth and adults (WHO 1996b). Around 95 per cent of those who suffer from tuberculosis live in developing countries. Most of them are poor. For example, in Soweto, South Africa, the incidence of TB is more than 100 times higher in low-income areas than in the high-income areas of the same city (Helmer 1992).

TB is spread by the TB bacillus. When a person with active TB coughs, TB bacilli pass into the air. Infection is most likely in closed and crowded rooms, usually in homes or the workplace. Sputum (spit) can also carry infection. Cattle can be infected with TB, and TB bacilli may be carried in milk which is not pasteurised. Where TB is common, half the population may be infected by the time they are adults, but only around 10 per cent of infected people will go on to develop active TB. There are two kinds of active TB; pulmonary TB (of the lungs) and non-pulmonary TB (of other parts of the body). One person with pulmonary TB will infect 20–28 other people on average before they either die or recover and two to three of those infected will develop TB. Without treatment, 60–70 per cent of those infected will die within five years (*Footsteps* 1994).

The only available vaccine, BCG, can protect children but does not work for adolescents or adults. Also, where there is HIV infection – with weakening of the immune system of the body – TB is increasing rapidly. TB may also hasten the progress of HIV into AIDS. In sub-Saharan Africa at least 3.8 million people are infected both with TB and HIV. In Asia, where 1.1 billion people suffer from TB (WHO 1995b), an explosion of co-infected people (those with HIV plus TB) is expected to rise significantly.

In most cases, drug treatment for TB costs as little as US$13–30 per person for a six month course. This can cure the infection, and stop the person transmitting it to others. But treatment has to be taken for six months, and many patients, once they start to feel better (but not yet cured) stop taking the full course of treatment. This risks recurrence, development of drug resistance and continuing spread of the disease. WHO estimates that only 30 per cent of all national TB programmes are applying the measures required to control the epidemic, and often low-cost drugs sit on shelves unused. A new strategy called DOTS (directly observed short course) could cure around 95 per cent of TB sufferers, and uses medicines costing less than US$11. Health workers watch as their patients swallow their medicines and track each patient, ensuring that contagious people are cured (WHO 1996b).

Intestinal helminths (worms)

Intestinal parasitic infections (commonly known as worms) are estimated to affect a quarter of the global population, mostly people in developing countries who come from poor and vulnerable groups. Worms are often companions to poor sanitation and children who are poor suffer particularly from worm infestations. This *worm burden* has effects on growth and cognitive function in children, and on development of girls and women. In East Africa, studies indicated small but significant changes in growth with worm-infested school children who did not have that worm burden (ascariasis, trichuris or hookworm) or infestation with intestinal helminths. Children with hookworm infections had growth stunting and delayed development, while intestinal helminths cause inflammation of the intestines. Chronic infammation results in growth failure, whether resulting from secondary effects on nutritional balance or by more direct effects on metabolism.

Although mortality from intestinal parasites is low, the absolute number of deaths is fairly high because so many people are infected. For example, in 1993 it is estimated that hookworm killed 90 000 people (WHO 1995b). The infections are spreading rapidly in slums, shanty towns and squatter settlements. Treatment is not expensive for intestinal parasites, but to be effective it must be accompanied by health education and action for safe drinking water and sanitation.

The continuing challenge of fighting these diseases

Fighting these diseases has always been an uphill battle, never more so than at present, where there are often critical shortages of finances, trained and experienced personnel and equipment. Sadly, even where trained personnel are available, they may be unable to function effectively without basic items such as slides with which to diagnose malaria, or bednets to initiate revolving community-based mosquito bednet systems. Due to poor or incomplete information, the real extent of these diseases may not be clear and this hinders the setting of targets and taking of practical action against the diseases.

There are some practical actions which the poor themselves can take to protect themselves from such diseases, like using bednets, screening doors and windows, removing mosquito-breeding sites, plastering the walls of their houses, getting full immunisation for their children, and installing safe water and sanitation as well as improving domestic hygiene practices. But in taking some of these actions they need technical advice and support and basic materials (e.g. bednets and permethrine). They also need local volunteer trained community health workers who are functionally linked to health staff and other collaborators. In such ways more sustainable local systems can be built to combat these diseases.

3.7 MENTAL DISORDERS AND THE POOR

Mental health in poorer countries has only recently been the focus of attention. It is calculated that mental retardation and epilepsy rates are three to five times higher in low-income than industrialised countries. It is further estimated that cases of schizophrenia in low-income countries will increase from over 16 million in 1985 to over 24 million by 2000 (Carnegie Foundation 1996). People at particular risk to mental disorders include street children, people who take habit-forming drugs and other addictive substances, those with problems arising from HIV infection and AIDS, internal migrants and people who have been displaced. Generally, mental health services have not been easily accessible to the poor, or of good quality. Mental patients often live far from where care is offered, and the poorer the mentally disordered person, the greater burden they often suffer. Poverty itself can also be an experience which scars the mind.

Family support may be an asset to a poor person with a chronic mental disorder, but urbanisation and other factors are undermining traditional family caring patterns. Some mental disorders are likely to recover when circumstances and conditions are altered. For example, depressive and psychosomatic disorders occurring among displaced and refugee populations are described as 'soft' mental disorders and occur more frequently among the poor than 'hard' mental disorders such as schizophrenia and dementia. People who are poor are said to value their physical health more than their mental health. In some places stigma still surrounds mental disorder and may delay seeking of treatment by family, friends and even health professionals for people who need it. Instead, those who are sick seek help from non-psychiatric doctors, who are not always trained in early recognition of certain mental disorders (Alegria *et al.* 1991). Developing countries commonly have few resources for mental health. For example, Mozambique had one psychiatrist for around 15 million people. Angola, also bearing the legacy of long conflict, and with a third of its health infrastructure destroyed by war, had no psychiatrist for around 10 million people. Training is underway, supported by WHO, for doctors in Portuguese speaking countries, covering a total population of 250 million.

FEASIBLE ACTION AGAINST ROOT CAUSES OF POVERTY

Twenty main causes of poverty were outlined in Chapter 2. This chapter begins by looking again at these, to consider whether they have older or newer roots, how the poor and vulnerable are affected in relation to health and what kind of action is feasible in trying to cut such roots. Some action can only be taken at international or national levels, but what action can be taken at district level and by whom? Next, the focus is on one factor which often influences the survival patterns and health of the rural poor. This is the often central role of livestock. The chapter then considers access of the poor to simple and appropriate health-related technologies which can help to cut some of the roots of ill health. Lastly, the focus is on access of the poor and vulnerable to basic education, one key to cutting some roots of poverty and improving household health.

4.1 POVERTY HAS DEEP ROOTS

Considering which roots of poverty are deep and which shallow, helps to indicate what action may be feasible against poverty and for health. For removing a weed with very long and strong roots, it is best to use a strong spade/stick which can cut deep into the earth. If not, the weed may appear to be removed, but deeper roots may remain, enabling the weed to grow again. For removing a weed with shallow roots, both weed and roots can be removed, preventing regrowth.

Which roots can be cut and how?

The roots of poverty are complex. Cutting some of them may depend on factors which are beyond the capacity of the poor and vulnerable themselves. Such roots, like unequal land distribution, are often the ones which spawned that poverty in the first place. If a society is not oriented towards equality, local attempts to obtain greater equity remain like islands in a sea of inequity. But what district/local action can make some difference to the health and wellbeing of people who are poor and vulnerable? What actions can be linked together to have greater benefit, directly or indirectly on such groups?

Twenty main causes of poverty – their roots and implications

The 20 main causes of poverty are rated according to the following key:
++   older root
+   newer root
***   serious health implications for poor and vulnerable
**   milder health implications for poor and vulnerable.

1 Unequal wealth distribution (++/***)

Where there are no policies to control amassing of wealth (money, property, businesses) by a minority, the majority who are poor are caught in a cycle of poverty. Unequal wealth distribution is usually linked to other inequities, like lack of employment for the poor, unjust financial rewards for work, unsafe working conditions in industries and enterprises – often owned by the wealthy minority. With national policies which attempt greater equity, such as redistribution of wealth and establishment of social safety nets, the poor have a chance of moving out of poverty.

District/local action may include development of popular organisations and labour unions to represent the interests of the poor, development of income-generating and credit and savings schemes, local industries, marketing systems to raise the income of the poor and, indirectly, their level of health.

2 Unemployment and underemployment (+/***)

In many developing countries rates of unemployment are high and many in employment are in low-paid, low productivity jobs. They often live in fear of job losses and falling wages, and their capacity to purchase basic necessities steadily declines. Women are particularly involved in precarious and underpaid work, with few labour organisations to protect their interests. The unemployed and underemployed household is at greater risk to factors which undermine physical and psychological health. A household where there is employment has a better chance to maintain its members' health, prevent disease and access health care when needed. Rapid population growth continues to outstrip the rate of employment opportunities being created. Where people climb the ladder of economic development, they tend to have smaller families, but caught in the cycle of poverty, large family size continues.

District/local action may include development of income-generating and credit and savings schemes, and small industries, food-for-work schemes, welfare schemes involving loans, livestock and other assets to increase the opportunities for employment and self employment.

3 Unequal land distribution and landlessness (++/***)

Linked to unequal wealth distribution, this poverty root reduces access of the poor to production of food crops or cash crops. Food is the raw material from which essential human growth takes place – whether a fetus or growing child. It is the fuel which keeps the human body functioning correctly and strengthens it to fight off infections and diseases. When disease occurs, food assists the body to recover. The urban poor without land often lack income to purchase food, particularly when they are female-headed households, as women have limited access to alternative sources of livelihood such as wage employment. Lack of secure land rights undermines access of the poor to other inputs, especially credit and extension services, for productive activities. For example, without land a farmer cannot get credit.

District/local action may include development of popular organisations to represent the interests of the landless and those owning unproductive land. Effectiveness of action will depend on current national policies on land and agrarian reform. For example, in some countries a wealthy minority continue to own the majority of the land. Sadly, even where land reform laws exist, they may not have been implemented. Wealthy elites often block implementation of land reform as not in their interests. In other places, there has been some success in increasing access to productive land by the poor.

Other district/local action may include subsidised food schemes and fair price shops. Also, developing alternative income-generating possibilities, like small industries, to reduce dependency on cash cropping.

4 Lack of access to capital/money (+/***)

In desperation, especially during times of ill health, the poor are often forced to turn to moneylenders and loan sharks who charge high interest rates. The poor are intimidated by mainstream banking systems. Lack of money/capital prevents the poor from maintaining health and preventing disease in the household/workplace. It reduces their access to health services and to early diagnosis of diseases/conditions, which then are more costly to treat.

District/local action in this area includes development of financial services and income-generating schemes for the poor at the same time as keeping the costs of health services within the affordable reach of the poor.

5 Continuing legacy of colonisation (++/**)

Wealthier nations continue to pursue actions according to their own self interests, whether they be for economic benefit, security, political or territorial concerns. Undersea nuclear testing goes ahead despite many protestations, particularly from those who live near the site or who will later be affected by it, while indigenous populations who are poor continue to be dispossessed and marginalised, deprived of human rights, their land, forests, culture and dignity. The tentacles of continuing colonisation continue to affect, directly or indirectly, the access of poor and vulnerable groups to many of their basic needs for health and wellbeing.

District/local action may include development of popular organisations to represent local interests, and monitoring of harmful health effects.

6 Globalisation of the world economy (+/**)

A small group of multinational enterprises continue to exercise disproportionate economic and cultural power over those less able to resist them, whether they deal in commodities such as oil, diamonds, copper, timber, tobacco or fast foods. There are said to be around 300 consortiums (multinational institutions and transnational corporations) and powerful regional trading blocs who, together, mainly control global productive assets, as well as the industries producing goods and services. People who are poor have practically no voice as far as globalisation is concerned. They are too often the raw material from which other people's economic gain is extracted. Their poverty results in reduced ability to maintain health and prevent disease or injury.

District/local action may include development of popular organisations to represent their interests, and formation of labour unions to demand fair wages and safer working conditions.

7 Structural adjustment (+/***)

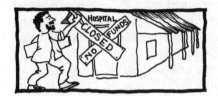

Structural adjustment programmes (SAPs), introduced in response to the world debt crisis in the early eighties generally required governments to take measures to stabilise their economies, and encourage economic growth and lower inflation rates. For the poor and vulnerable population, the effects of the SAPs have yet to be fully assessed but have included removal of food subsidies and introduction of user fees for health services.

District/local action may include introduction/refining of exemption system for user fees for people/households which are poor and vulnerable. If food subsidies or social welfare schemes have been removed, district/local income generation, food crop production to benefit the poor and locally organised and funded social welfare activities may also be needed.

8 Continuing industrial and technological revolutions (+/**)

Changes in industry and technology which have reduced the need for human labour (such as farm machinery or robots in factories) directly affect the poor, who have limited access to employment or training for the new technologies. Unemployment and underemployment affects their capacity to maintain health or prevent disease.

District/local level action may include increasing productive employment schemes such as development of small-scale industries and enterprises, income generation, financial services and loans for the poor, credit and savings schemes, basic training for employment and business management, and development of marketing systems.

9 Lack of decision making on governance (+/**)

For poor and vulnerable groups, access to the electoral system is not simply a matter of voting. Change through the ballot box is often elusive, for example voting procedures can be undermined through irregularities and intimidation. If the poor are marginalised from such processes they have no opportunity to influence politicians and social policies, including those relating to health, from which they might benefit.

At district/local level, whether the poor and vulnerable are able to participate in decision making on governance will depend on factors such as existence of corrupt leaders/practices, access to protection for exercise of voting rights and existence of organisations to represent their interests.

10 Violation of human rights (+/**)

Violence is increasing in many places and its main victims are almost always civilians, especially the poor and vulnerable. Human rights violations include torture and rape as well as injuries/fatalities incurred in mines. Civil and ethnic conflict disrupts health services and restricts population movements, for example by preventing patients/ambulances reaching medical assistance. Violence and human rights abuses aggravate the already negative effects of poverty, including the often poor health status of the local population. They have also affected professional and voluntary health workers who serve the poor and vulnerable groups, some of whom have paid with their lives. Many violations of human rights go unpunished, and the poor and vulnerable usually have little access to legal aid or justice.

District/local action may include setting up low-cost legal aid options for the poor, recording of human rights violations, provision of counselling and care for victims of human rights abuses.

11 Environmental degradation (+/***)

Environmental degradation is a newer and deadly root cause of poverty. Two types of environmental degradation affect poverty and health. The first relates to the natural environment (such as degraded soil, polluted fresh water, deforestation, depleted ozone layer) and the second, to the man-made environment (urban pollution of air through carbon monoxide and unsustainable use of non-renewable energy sources, such as oil, natural gas, minerals and metals). The effects of environmental degradation are particularly felt by the poor who tend to live in environmentally vulnerable areas. The health effects of environmental damage on the poor include food shortages and malnutrition, water-related diseases, ill health caused by eating products of polluted oceans (such as infected shellfish), poisoning by pesticides and fertilisers and respiratory diseases resulting from air pollution.

District/local action against environmental degradation may include formation of organisations to represent local interests, reafforestation, protection of water sources, use of more sustainable agricultural practices and action to protect coastal waters and marine produce.

12 Race and class discrimination (++/***)

Discrimination against a particular class or race is an ancient plague in human society. It includes discrimination against indigenous people in conquered lands, against sections of a society which are poor and vulnerable, and enslaved or virtually enslaved people/households (for instance, as encouraged by the bonded labour system). It underpins many injustices and inequalities which influence access by the poor and vulnerable to food production, safe water, adequate shelter and what they need to maintain health, prevent disease and seek assistance when they need it.

District and local action may include formation of organisations to represent their interests, and collaboration with national and other NGOs in educational, income-generating, health and human rights schemes.

13 Degradation of indigenous cultures (+/**)

Governments and business enterprises have often seen indigenous land as empty space awaiting occupation and development. Indigenous people are often regarded as obstacles to modern development and even where guarantees for the rights of indigenous people have been obtained, they have often been violated. The effects of degradation of indigenous cultures include lack of access to land for production of food crops or cash crops, unemployment or poorly paid employment, violence, lack of safe water and sanitation, poor nutrition, reduced access to social services and marginalisation from decision making on development which affects their wellbeing.

District/local action may include formation of organisations to represent their interests and rights, and collaboration with government and/or NGOs over education, health, income generation, agriculture and livestock, and human rights violations.

14 Natural disasters (++/***)

Natural hazards, such as earthquakes and floods, can directly or indirectly affect people who are poor by, for example, flooding farmland, destroying crops, affecting drinking water supply, destroying lives, shelter, possessions and means of livelihood. The poorest of the poor may be forced to migrate to urban slums. The poorer people become, the more their vulnerability to a variety of hazards and disasters increases, for example the more flimsily constructed the dwelling, the greater the destruction. The poor have more difficulty in recovering from a disaster, particularly if their livelihood is affected.

District/local action may include siting of dwellings in safer locations, use of stronger materials and designs, building of dykes to control flooding, early-warning systems for typhoons, preparation of first aid and survival items against hazards and disasters, formation of local groups to mitigate disaster effects and food-for-work programmes.

15 Man-made disasters e.g. war and conflict (+/***)

People who are poor are often the principal victims of man-made disasters. For example, they are made homeless and forced to flee as refugees or they reap a later deadly harvest of unexploded landmines. The health effects of man-made disasters are wide ranging and include disrupted and destroyed health services, death or disabilities and lack of access to food, safe water, shelter, or security. Often, emergency relief for refugee and displaced populations is overstretched, reducing access by those who need them.

District/local action usually depends on the prevailing power during and after the period of conflict. It may take many years to rehabilitate health services in order to provide adequate safe water, shelter and food supplies. In some places there are UN-sponsored and NGO initiatives underway to rebuild wartorn societies.

16 Gender discrimination (++/***)

Gender discrimination often begins early among the poor, with preference for sons and reduced food and care for girls, who are often the first to drop out of school and may marry early to begin early child bearing. In many cases women suffer disproportionately from the effects of structural adjustment programmes, loss of livelihood, environmental degradation and from violence, including within the home. Because poor women often bear most if not all the responsibility for child raising, the health and wellbeing of poor children is also affected by the increasing feminisation of poverty. Women who are poor often neglect their own health or seek assistance for a health problem at a late stage.

Action at district/local level may include educational schemes for school-age girls and adult women, income-generating and credit and savings schemes and family planning, including use of natural methods, safe abortion options, safe motherhood and newborn care, plus learning about approaches and methods to protect themselves from HIV infection and other sexually transmitted diseases.

17 Violence in the home and outside (+/**)

Violence is increasing in many places, often fuelled by the degradations and frustrations of poverty. The poor are the least protected and most exposed to violence. In the family/household setting, violence includes physical injury, sexual abuse, burnings and psychological and emotional abuse. Violence directed at men may be linked to exploitative labour systems (such as bonded labour) activities of criminal gangs, alcoholism, drugs and military or police brutality. Child abuse includes physical abuse and injury (such as poisoning), neglect, emotional abuse and sexual abuse.

District/local action against violence may include special training for the police, health workers, teachers, local leaders, increasing access of the poor to low-cost or free legal advice and assistance, and creating opportunities for the problem of violence to be examined.

18 No access to education and training (+/**)

The poor were traditionally denied opportunities for education and training. More recently, such opportunities have been undercut by education cutbacks and introduction of fees for schooling. Poor children are often the first to drop out of school and there are fewer poor children in secondary or further education. Links between education and health include lower mortality rates for infants whose mothers have had some education and opportunities for school-age children to learn about family life/sex education, family planning and spacing, and ways to protect themselves from sexually transmitted diseases including HIV. Education and training can provide paths out of poverty.

District/local action may include innovative school systems to reach the children who are poor, out-of-school children schemes, income-generating schemes for raising funds to pay school fees or support poor children in secondary or further education, adult and lifelong educational opportunities, and opportunities for retraining, where necessary.

19 No access to health services and social welfare (+/***)

The poor are finding it harder to get health care and social welfare, which themselves have been undercut by shrinking budgets. Health sector reforms are trying to streamline public health services, but in the process a large share of the responsibility for providing basic social and health services is being passed to inexperienced local governments, or to the needy groups themselves.

District/local action may include participatory needs assessment, planning, implementation and monitoring of subsequent action. Action may include developing community-managed water and sanitation systems, improving production of food crops, introduction of local weaning foods and increasing access to family planning and spacing. Also helpful would be the introduction or refining of fee exemptions for the poor, subsidising selected services, introduction of revolving drug funds, training of community-based health volunteers, mobile and outreach services and innovative schemes to get medical equipment health staff who work most closely with poor and vulnerable groups.

20 No access to water for drinking and irrigation (+/***)

Despite strenuous efforts to ensure access to safe drinking water for people in developing countries, progress in reaching the unserved has been poor since 1990. Rapid population growth, slow coverage expansion and unplanned urbanisation has also led to inadequate safe water supplies. Water availability is fundamental to health and hygienic practices. Water-related diseases continue to undermine the lives and wellbeing of the poor.

District/local action may include development of community-managed water systems for safe drinking water as well as irrigation of food and small-scale cash crops, and watering of livestock. Sanitation systems (such as pit latrines) will need to be installed at the same time if full impact on health is to be achieved.

4.2 LIVESTOCK IN THE LIVES OF THE POOR

Why are livestock so important in the lives of the poor? Owning many animals is wealth. Sale of small livestock, such as sheep, goats, poultry (chickens, ducks) can supplement a meagre household income. Having draught animals to plough increases productivity. Animal power is used for pumping water and post-harvest processing. Animals which help in hunting provide food for the household. Income from livestock includes not only cash sales of animals but also sale of manure for fuel, or fertiliser made from animal excrement, bone, feather or horn, and services such as ploughing and transport. Tools such as leather harnesses or bone implements are often made from animal products. Livestock also represent an insurance policy against hard times – a store of wealth which can be converted into cash or exchanged when a small income is needed to survive. Livestock can be an asset to be exchanged or consumed for a special celebration. This is why the owning of livestock has developed such deep cultural and religious significance in many developing societies.

The economies of some developing countries are very much dependent on livestock, but ecological changes have had profound effects on livestock numbers and national economies. For nomadic poor families living in drier areas, livestock represents their major source of income and often their only capital asset. Small homestead livestock such as sheep, goats, chickens and pigs are characterised by low per capita maintenance requirements, unlike horses and water buffaloes. The former are able to scavenge for food and usually need less herding and supervision. In nomadic pastoral societies, the needs of livestock determine the location and movement of whole population groups as they and their animals seek water and pasture in an interdependent survival pattern.

Inputs by the poor into their livestock include food, water, safety and protection, shelter, attention to animal health, equipment (for ploughing, perhaps) and processing (such as milk processing or meat preparation). Outputs include food, fuel, income, agriculture, shelter (hides, manure for floor and walls), clothing (such as wool, leather, fur, silk), transport, companionship, security (dogs and geese) and ceremonial uses. In some countries animals even provide warmth during the winter (where cattle and other livestock live in an adjoining stable)

Livestock provide power and fuel for the poor

In many countries, much labour used for agriculture is contributed by livestock. Animals are often more important than tractors, especially in Latin America and Southeast Asia, where buffalo are vital to the rice economy. Around four million draught animals in developing countries directly or indirectly serve two billion people. Draught animals include cattle, buffaloes, horses, mules, camels, yaks and donkeys, which are used to cultivate up to half of the total area cropped in developing countries. They also pull millions of carts. Recently, the value of the donkey to the poor has been rediscovered.

Why families depend on livestock

Transport
- Carrying goods and people.

Water/health
- Transporting water.
- Soap from animal products.
- Pigs as scavengers.

Fuel
- Dung/manure.
- Carrying wood.

Income
- Represent wealth.
- Act as investments.
- Sale of services, e.g. ploughing.
- Sale of dung/manure.
- Sale of animals.

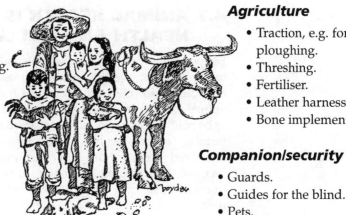

Agriculture
- Traction, e.g. for ploughing.
- Threshing.
- Fertiliser.
- Leather harness.
- Bone implements.

Food
- Meat/blood.
- Milk.
- Eggs.
- Fish.
- Transporting food.

Companion/security
- Guards.
- Guides for the blind.
- Pets.
- Used for mental health therapy.

Clothing
- Hides/leather/skins.
- Wool.
- Feathers.

Shelter
- Manure for floors and walls.
- Skins for tents.
- Kept for warmth.

Ceremonial
- Gives owner status.
- Used for dowry.
- Eaten at festivals.

(First published in *Community Development Journal* (1987).)

What women and children contribute to livestock production

In many places, caring for small animals such as chickens, rabbits, guinea pigs and goats is predominantly the work of women and children. Even where the herding and care of animals is largely men's work, women may be responsible for milking and processing milk, collecting fodder, drying cow dung for fuel and caring for the lactating, young or sick animals. In some places women care for cattle. Women and children have to integrate their livestock production with a wide range of other responsibilities, such as caring for the young and for older people. Poultry and small animals are often the only source of income fully under the control of women. Such livestock raised by women often make a greater contribution to the diet of low-income groups than do cattle.

Sadly, few livestock extension programmes in 1990 were said to include women (FAO 1990) and there was a shortage of female extension officers. But some programmes have linked sale of milk to training women responsible for caring for the cows. In Yemen, a female extension expert and ten local women were employed as extension agents in highland areas. In addition to teaching improved farming and improved small livestock rearing techniques, they were also involved in literacy work and broader advice on health and nutrition (ODA 1986).

4.3 ANIMAL HEALTH IS LINKED TO HUMAN HEALTH AND WELLBEING

For poor livestock farmers and households with a single cow or buffalo, the injury, death or infertility of the animal can be an economic catastrophe. So also can its lowered production of milk or inability to work. A draught animal which dies in the first few months after acquisition may still have to be paid for over several years – even though it contributed nothing to the farming family's income. Thus, access to simple medicines and training in improved animal husbandry techniques can enable poor farmers to increase their income and retain some control over their survival. Some livestock insurance schemes introduced at small farm level have proved useful.

What do livestock need to keep healthy?

The basic needs of livestock are very similar to the basic needs of humans. Animals need food, water, health care and shelter for living and sleeping. Some also need protection from accident, predators or theft. Animals may thus compete with people for community resources. Where resources are limited both humans and animals suffer, such as in the case of scarce water supplies. Good water supplies which are not infested by disease-causing organisms are required, and milk-producing animals have the greatest need for clean water. There must be sufficient food for animals in an area as well as water, though there are dangers of over grazing close to watering points unless control of animals is maintained. Also needed are measures to control insects and infectious diseases which can affect animals. In the mid eighties it was estimated that at least five per cent of cattle, 10 per cent of sheep and goats, and 15 per cent of pigs died annually of disease (FAO 1983).

Health services and barefoot vets for the poor

The poor need services designed to maintain the health of their livestock. Most developing countries train Animal Health Assistants (AHAs) during a two-year course. Community members have also received basic training to practise as *barefoot vets*. Success of such schemes has been mixed due to the quality of training and youth of school leavers with low community standing. On the other hand, where older and respected community livestock owners have had their skills and knowledge upgraded, they have provided basic services to other livestock owners and trained them in improved animal husbandry techniques. For example, nomadic scouts have been appointed and paid for by village communities in Ethiopia, Madagascar and Niger to provide low-cost animal health services.

The zoonoses – links between animal and human health

Over 150 diseases which affect animals can also affect humans. These human diseases with animal sources are known as *zoonoses*. They can be transmitted to people through animal bites, direct or indirect contact with living or dead animals and animal products such as meat, milk, eggs, wool or hides. They can also be transmitted through eating foods from animal sources, particularly foods prepared carelessly or inadequately cooked. The persons most vulnerable to zoonoses are farm families and other people closely associated with agricultural occupations, such as veterinarians, livestock inspectors, those who handle animal food products (such as butchers), foresters, hunters, those who care for sick animals, refugees and those living in temporary crowded conditions with animals. Not only is the health of human food producers affected, but also the animals themselves are unable to produce meat or dairy products, or to work (Schwabe 1981).

Sometimes man-made changes in the landscape or environment can increase danger from zoonoses. For example, diseases resulting in much sickness and death have been reported from irrigation projects, artificial lakes, areas of deforestation and railway and road construction sites. In South America, deforestation to create cattle-breeding pastures resulted in introducing vampire bats, and with them rabies. Factors which also increase risk from zoonoses include the greatly expanded international and national trade in live animals, animal products and animal feedstuffs, which facilitate spread of infection. Others are poor animal housing, limited water supplies and lack of adequate food storage methods or waste disposal, especially in expanding urban areas which may be infested with rats. When animals live close to humans it is useful to consider some basic rules for raising and handling animals.

Twelve ways to avoid the zoonoses

1 Keep animals in clean, well-ventilated quarters, if possible separate from where the family eats and sleeps.

2 Keep water and animal feed safe from harmful agents.

3 If possible cook garbage and refuse used for animal feed.

4 Keep the place where food is produced very clean, especially in the case of meat and eggs.

5 If human faeces are eaten by pigs or spread on fields, animals may get sick.

6 Avoid being splattered with animal urine and faeces by wearing protective clothing which can be washed regularly.

7 Make sure new animals, purchased for breeding, are healthy.

8 Examine existing animals regularly and remove sick ones.

9 Do not butcher sick animals for eating or selling.

10 When diseased animals die or abort their offspring, bury them or burn them, preferably on the advice of a vet, livestock officer or village barefoot vet trained to give primary animal health care.

11 Do not bleed such animals to avoid contamination and infection.

12 After disposal of animals, clean and preferably disinfect your hands and the premises.

(Adapted from *Community Development Journal* (1987).)

4.4 TECHNOLOGY APPROPRIATE TO THE NEEDS OF POOR HOUSEHOLDS

To be useful and used by people, technology needs to fulfil a practical use to fit with the local culture, and be maintained by those who use it most. It is also important that the technology – whether it is a tool or a method of doing something – is affordable by the household and the community, and optimally made from locally available materials, using local skills. The need for a particular technology should be identified at household/community level. If those who want to use it participate in developing it, they are more likely to feel a sense of ownership, and responsibility. *Appropriate technology*, if imposed from outside, can become inappropriate.

What kinds of appropriate technology do poor households and communities need to maintain their health and prevent disease? How can several technologies be introduced to maximise the good effect of each? What is available and affordable in a particular locality? These questions are briefly explored and some examples provided to stimulate action.

Technologies for food and nutrition

Food and nutrition are the foundations on which physical health are built and maintained, through eating the right volume and composition of foods prepared to retain essential ingredients needed by the body. This also helps to prevent disease. Appropriate technologies for poor households include those for food production. Examples are agricultural tools designed for women, ploughs, harnesses for animal traction, improved seeds, and local methods for composting and pest control. Methods for raising poultry, rabbits and guinea pigs, and establishing fish ponds also contribute to household and cash food production. Appropriate technologies for harvesting include low-cost milling, grinding, winnowing and husking of cereals, and shelling of nuts.

For processing, preserving and storing foods, technologies include drying of vegetables, and smoking or salting of fish. There are technologies and approaches to retain nutritional value of foods, prepare new types and combinations of weaning foods, reduce use of fuelwood and reduce harmful smoke inside dwellings. The best ways to store food include improved granaries, woven and earthenware containers. There are also ways to protect food from disease-causing vectors such as flies (making of fly covers, small screened cupboards or boxes or woven food covers) and to protect household food from cockroaches and rats. Lastly, there are ways to keep cooking areas free of rubbish and food scraps, and to make local soap and utensil racks to keep eating and cooking utensils clean.

Technologies for adequate shelter

Adequate shelter protects human health and prevents disease. In Chapter 3 the essentials for adequate shelter were presented, plus the diseases/conditions which can arise without it. Appropriate technologies for ensuring adequate shelter include methods of constructing low-cost dwellings appropriate to the needs of poor and vulnerable households. Optimally, the community itself should be involved in design and construction of dwellings, and in use of new combinations of locally available materials. Appropriate technology includes siting and constructing dwellings to withstand possible natural hazards (such as earthquakes, mudslides, flooding or typhoons). There must also be attention to size, light and ventilation (windows, siting of door), as well as to security (of door(s) and window(s)). For the poor, materials used in construction of the dwellings need to be durable.

Respiratory diseases and eye conditions can be caused by a smoky interior. Appropriate technologies include use of smokeless stoves and smoke exits. To avoid disease-causing vectors such as mosquitoes, low-cost ways exist for screening doors and windows with fly-wire or netting and killing flies through simple fly traps and fly swats. Rats can be controlled by blocking passageways through which they may enter storage areas, and using rat traps. Malaria-causing mosqitoes can be controlled by destroying breeding areas such as pools or containers of stagnant water near dwellings. Appropriate technology includes using low-cost mosquito nets (if possible, impregnated with the insecticide permethrine).

Poisons and insecticides should be used with great care and only when necessary. Be sure to wash thoroughly after using them. Keep them away from children, food and animals. All solid rubbish or dead animals need to be buried/burned.

Technologies for safe water and sanitation

Along with food and nutrition, safe water and sanitation are foundations on which good health is built and maintained. The appropriateness of technologies for safe water and sanitation will depend on many local circumstances, such as terrain (mountainous, perhaps, or coastal with salinity of groundwater) and water sources (whether river, rainwater, spring or underground). For example, in a mountainous area a gravity-feed system may be constructed to bring upland water down through bamboo pipes to a village. In a shanty town, water may be piped from a lake to communal standpipes. In either type of situation, tanks (cement, aluminium) may be used for rainwater catchment. Hand drilling may be used to construct wells in more arid areas. Such technologies harvest water for human and livestock consumption.

Areas which suffer from water shortages for crops and livestock may lose water which falls as rain through wastage, run-off and evaporation. The principle of water harvesting is to catch as much of this rainfall as possible and hold it efficiently for later use. This can be done through run-off farming (rainwater is channelled from a slope into small cropped area or tank), small catchment dams for rainwater (bottom sealed with clay, plastic or cement), micro-catchments (same principle as dam but smaller scale, for instance rainwater may be directed at a particular tree/shrub), tie ridging (creating small basins in which crops can grow), underground tanks (designed to catch water from flash floods), catchment tanks (of brick, cement, concrete), weirs which check or divert small rivers, and springs (captured and channelled into chamber/tank/piping system). For household use water harvesting may include construction of gravity-fed upland water catchment systems to supply communal or domestic standpipes, and the digging or hand-drilling of wells.

The next group of technologies relates to protecting and maintaining a safe water supply, such as keeping animals away from springs and standpipe surroundings, basic maintenance and repair, and protection of water outlets (for instance good drainage around standpipes). Household drinking water should be safely stored, for example with a cover or lid for earthen pot. To avoid contamination of water, a clean dipping ladle/tin/mug/ coconut shell/gourds are needed. Accompanying hygiene education is important concerning water protection, such as not defecating or washing clothes in a river where drinking water is also drawn.

The appropriateness of technologies for safe disposal of human excreta and urine also depend on local circumstances. In some places hand-dug pit latrines may be the best and most affordable option. Correct design of a pit toilet is essential. For example it must be allocated at least six metres from a dwelling and at least 30 metres and downhill from any drinking water source. A cover keeps insects and water away from the excreta and urine in the pit. It is also important to leave a space between roof and walls for ventilation and light. There are also pour-flush pit latrines, where water is poured into the pit after passing stools, a specially designed bend in the pipe preventing unpleasant odours reaching from pit into the latrine. Another design is a double-pit latrine system which collects stools separately from urine, the stools later being used as compost. Other technologies linked to proper use of safe water and maintenance of health include soap making, tooth sticks for brushing teeth, soap containers and locally made toothbrush/tooth stick holders.

From Experience

In Papua New Guinea during a community-based joint training course for volunteer village health workers and health staff from aid posts (small clinics), the checklist on p. 83 was used to help participants reflect on their own households and whether basic health needs were being met.

Technologies for maternal and child health

Appropriate technologies which can make a difference to maternal health include *home-based women's health records*, which are kept by women

```
┌──────────────────────────────────────────────────────────────┐
│ KLIN BODY - KLIN HAUS (Clean Body ~ Clean House)             │
├──────────────────────────────────────────────────────────────┤
│ 1 Wash body every day        □   12 Got rats            □    │
│ 2 Brush teeth every day      □   13 Got mosquitoes      □    │
│ 3 Wash clothes often         □   14 Use mosquito net    □    │
│ 4 Sleep 8 hours              □   15 Long grass near house □   │
│ 5 Eat 3 times a day          □   16 Got latrine (pit)   □    │
│ 6 Wash hands before eating   □   17 Latrine got cover   □    │
│ 7 Wash hands after toilet    □   18 Got chicken pen     □    │
│ 8 House has smoke hole       □   19 Got pig pen         □    │
│ 9 House has window           □                               │
│ 10 Roof keeps out rain       □                               │
│ 11 Got cockroaches           □                               │
└──────────────────────────────────────────────────────────────┘
```

(aged 15–64) at home, showing for each woman their pre-pregnancy health profile, the record of their pregnancies, deliveries plus care after birth, family planning profile, health status between pregnancies and post-menopausal health. There are many types of home-based records, developed from a WHO prototype based on Indian experience.

A trained traditional birth attendant (TBA) can also be considered as appropriate technology. She/he may use a locally made wooden measuring stick to determine if a pregnant woman is below a specific height (145 cm) and therefore at risk of a complicated delivery. The TBA may use a locally made bottle holder to heat a pregnant woman's urine to check it for protein at home during pregnancy. A ready prepared simple birth kit (three clean cord ties, two pieces of cotton wool/clean cloth, a clean razor blade, two pointed nail-cleaning sticks and a piece of soap wrapped in a clean cloth) can increase the likelihood of a cleaner home delivery and reduce risk of infection for mother and newborn.

Appropriate technologies for child health include keeping at home simple measuring utensils (spoons) and ingredients for making home-based rehydration fluid, sometimes called *sugar water*, though it may also contain a very small amount of salt. This is frequently a child lifesaver in home treatment of simple diarrhoea. Sometimes, local spoons (wood/tin/clay) are specially made for measuring correct amounts of sugar and salt then mixed with boiled and cooled drinking water. Sometimes this measuring device, can be attached by string/woven fibre to a standard measuring vessel (such as a litre plastic bottle or tin mug) to be used exclusively for making up oral rehydration fluid. Where sugar is not available sugar cane syrup can be used. Another way to rehydrate and nourish a sick child is by giving rice water, coconut water or local clear soups. Having this simple technology ready at hand increases the likelihood and frequency of use. Other appropriate technologies include a three-coloured mid upper-arm circumference measuring strip for children one to four years of age, and a hanging scale or local weighing device to regularly monitor the weight and growth of infants and young children.

LOOKING AT YOUR OWN PLACE

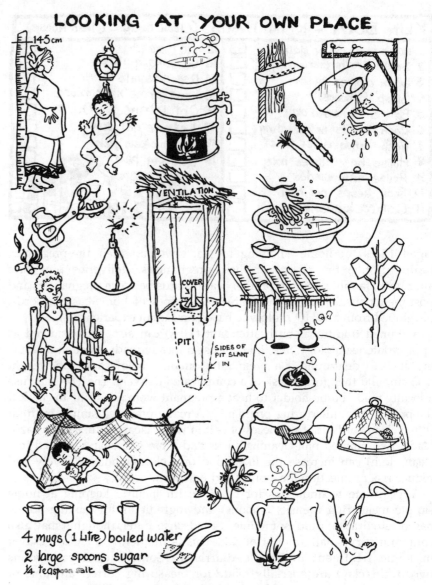

4 mugs (1 Litre) boiled water
2 large spoons sugar
¼ teaspoon salt

1 Measuring stick to see if a pregnant woman is below 145 cm in height.

2 Portable hanging scale for infants and young children.

3 Strip (three colours) for measuring mid-arm circumference of children aged one to four years (made from old X-ray film).

4 Wood-fuelled water heater made from used oil/petrol drum.

5 Family soap container made from old tin.

6 'Tippy tap' made from used plastic container, string/twine, nails for washing hands after using a latrine/defecating.

7 Dental probe made from tin/bamboo/twine and teeth-brushing stick.

8 Simple bottle-holding tongs for heating pregnant woman's urine (to test for protein).

9   Small kerosene lamp made from old tin with cloth/wool wick.

10 Pit latrine from local materials, with door, covered hole and ventilation.

11 Bowl (soap if possible) and water for hand washing before preparing food or breastfeeding.

12 Covered container protecting clean and safe drinking water.

13 Bamboo support seat for disabled child.

14 Stove with pipe for exit of smoke from cooking area/dwelling.

15 Branch holding drinking containers for drying and storing.

16 Mosquito net, especially to protect children and pregnant women from getting malaria.

17 Clay made into shape so that disabled worker can hold instruments better.

18 Food cover (bamboo and cotton netting) to prevent flies/insects from contaminating food.

19 Traditional leaves/seeds made into solution to treat minor cuts and wounds.

20 Home-made oral rehydration solution (Use four mugs (one litre) of boiled and cooled water mixed with two large spoonfuls of sugar, plus a **tiny** quarter teaspoon of salt, or one mug of boiled, cooled water with two palmfuls of sugar plus a tiny finger-pinch of salt. **This liquid should not taste saltier than human tears**).

Technologies for first aid

For the poor and vulnerable, taking appropriate first aid measures for minor and major injuries in the household or on the farm can sometimes reduce impact (further injury, undue bleeding, infection) and cost of the injuries, as well as save life. Helpful technologies include use of traditional local medicines and treatments for first aid. These might include treatments made from leaves, traditional teas or special compresses. Keeping a ready prepared simple first aid kit is also helpful. It should contain clean cloth to stop bleeding, bind a wound, tie a broken limb to a support (branch/plank of wood), boiled water, soap and even a pair of scissors or analgesics. Common household accidents include cuts and burns.

Technologies to prevent common local diseases/conditions/disabilities

Avoiding common local diseases can increase the survival chances of poor households. For example, even poor households have proved willing to buy low-cost mosquito nets. Optimally they should be impregnated with the insecticide permethrine, but this may not be easy to obtain by health services who guide households as to its proper use. If a poor household cannot afford nets for everybody, young children and pregnant women – for whom malaria is particularly dangerous – should receive priority. Other types of appropriate technologies include disability aids, such as locally made wheelchairs, artificial limbs, handgrips to assist people with leprosy to hold tools and eating utensils. (Chapter 8 contains more on coping with disability and poverty).

From Experience

In Bangladesh, the BRAC non-formal primary education approach mushroomed in five years to 12 000 centres serving 360 000 children of poor and non-literate rural families. Village management committees and parent–teacher associations were linked to the centres. Most teachers were women and 70 per cent of pupils were girls. Modest thatched huts with earthen floors accommodated around 30 pupils. For younger school drop-out children, three-year equivalent primary education was offered. For older ones, longer equivalent primary education was offered. Cost was US$18 per child – quarter of the normal fee. Classes were three hours daily. Materials provided were designed for real conditions of pupils and teachers.

From Experience

A mobile teachers programme in the northern Philippines was designed to target poor families in remote, rugged mountainous areas. Ethnic minorities in the sparsely populated area welcomed specially trained teachers who came to teach their children three days a week. Small classes couldn't justify a full-time teacher. Forty per cent of children were school drop outs or non-attenders. Each teacher visited two centres, which were open spaces or family houses. Seven hundred children were served by 31 teachers. Basic materials and desks were provided. Parents, actively involved, wanted to be taught themselves.

4.5 PRIMARY EDUCATION AND REACHING THE UNREACHED

For families who are poor, obtaining basic education for their children is often a distant dream. They may rate education as a basic need, along with food, water, land and shelter, but may have little access to it. Despite enormous efforts over the past decades by governments and agencies, access to basic education for the poor is still fraught with problems. Education budgets are being cut and the number of teachers is often insufficient, especially in remoter areas.

Reaching the unreached through non-formal education

Many of the children who drop out of school (or who never enter it in the first place) belong to socially disadvantaged groups, like urban and rural poor, ethnic, racial or religious minorities, nomadic communities, those living in isolated geographical areas, refugees and other displaced populations. By focusing directly on basic learning needs of participant target groups and on how they should be met, innovative non-formal education approaches have been developed. In many countries there is now greater flexibility in curricula, school time-tables, multigrade teaching, school management and school–community relations. Page 86 shows examples of approaches which are meeting the needs of the poor in particular places.

POLICIES AND PLANS AGAINST POVERTY AND FOR HEALTH

What types of policies and laws are needed relating to poverty and health, and how are they connected to the human life cycle? How can corruption undermine such policies and laws? These questions are addressed first in the chapter. The way in which development policies and plans can have negative effects on people who are poor and vulnerable is examined through looking at tourism. Next, the focus is on participatory development, through which the poor themselves prioritise their needs and retain better control over the development process. The often uneasy fit between bottom-up and top-down planning is examined. NGO policy and planning perspectives are outlined, along with some principles and practices for strengthening interaction between NGOs and government. The next focus is on planning for better access by the poor to financial services and credit, and finally, on links between increased income for women and improved family health.

5.1 MAIN POLICIES AND LAWS RELATING TO THE HUMAN LIFE CYCLE

Policies and laws directly or indirectly relating to poverty and health affect various groups at different stages in the human life cycle. For example, those relating directly to health of adolescents and young people who are poor may include those dealing with protection of workers' health, contraception and drugs. Indirect policies and laws may relate to minimum marriage age and prostitution.

Policies and laws relating to the human life cycle of the poor

The following table provides examples of main types of policies and laws which directly relate to health during the human life cycle of the poor, as well, in some cases, as a few examples of indirect policies and laws. The table can also be used to analyse what is available – or needs to be available – in a particular country/province/district.

POVERTY-RELATED POLICIES AND LAWS DIRECTLY AFFECTING HEALTH DURING THE STAGES OF THE HUMAN LIFE CYCLE

Purpose of policy	*Example of law*

Stage 1   Pre-conception and contraception

1	Forbidding of female genital mutilation.	Practice of female circumcision is a punishable offence.
2	Provision of appropriate contraceptive methods for poor and vulnerable women.	Specific contraceptives to be provided free/at low cost to low-income groups.

Stage 2   Pregnancy and early fetal growth

1	Establishment of minimum age for marriage.	Legal marriage age for girls, 18 and boys, 20 years.
2	Provision of safer pregnancy termination of unplanned pregnancies for poor women.	Selected health centres in remote areas permitted to carry out pregnancy termination under certain conditions.
3	Definition of minimal antenatal care for poor women.	Eligible women are entitled to minimum of three free antenatal visits.
4	Regulation of volunteer health workers, e.g. TBAs.	TBAs permitted to conduct home deliveries after training.
5	Prohibition of female infanticide.	Criminal offence to carry out gender determination through ultrasound.

Policies and laws **indirectly** affecting the human life cycle during this stage relate to: provision of sex/family life education as a compulsory subject in primary and secondary school curricula; prohibition of child marriage; prohibition of the dowry system; and permitting health staff to engage in private practice.

Stage 3 Childbirth and welfare of mother and newborn

1	Increase access for poor women to trained delivery assistance.	Production of minimum number of midwives annually and training of TBAs/home birth attenders.
2	Increase access to essential obstetric emergency care.	All district hospitals to be equipped for obstetric emergency care and maternity waiting homes to be established.
3	Reduce maternal and newborn death rate.	Compulsory maternal/newborn death case investigations.

| 4 | Motivation of health professionals to serve in peripheral services. | Period of compulsory rural service following graduation. |
| 5 | Encouragement of breastfeeding to prevent infant deaths. | Forbidding manufacture or importation of breastmilk substitutes. |

Policies and laws **indirectly** affecting this stage of the life cycle relate to: greater equity in allocating health care professionals plus incentives for them to serve in remoter areas or opportunities to specialise in general practice; prevention of sale or adoption of newborn infants of women who are poor; and upgrading of vital statistics system with compulsory birth and death registration.

Stage 4 Early infancy (up to five years)

1	Increase access to child health services, including immunisation against preventable childhood diseases.	Free services for children under five years.
2	Prevention of malnutrition among children in drought-affected areas.	Provision of free supplementary feeding.
3	Eliminate discrimination in favour of the girl child.	Monitoring of abortion of female fetuses and newborn deaths.

Stage 5 Childhood (6–14 years)

1	Prevention of dental caries. of public water supplies.	Compulsory fluoridation.
2	Prevention of food-borne diseases.	Compulsory certification by health inspectors of roadside food vendors.
3	Elimination of child prostitution, prosecution of adult offenders and traffickers.	Strict enforcement of criminal law on child prostitution, trafficking, sale and prostitution.
4	Avoidance of work-related accidents and injuries. hours, including in the informal sector, e.g. small businesses.	Prohibition of work in hazardous conditions and for long/ unsociable
5	Provision of services for disabled children.	Health staff trained to work with children with physical or mental disabilities.

Indirect policies and laws include: access to non-formal primary education for children unable to attend school (because they may be carrying out necessary tasks, such as caring for livestock); creation of training/ employment/health schemes and outreach services for children who live and work on the street; control of labour exploitation of children through minimum age for work and wages; and monitoring/regulating health effects of child labour.

Stage 6 Adolescence (15–24 years)

| 1 | Increase access to reproductive health services, e.g. contraception and education about sexually transmitted diseases including HIV/AIDS. | Provision of youth outreach services and drop-in centres. |

2 Reduction of abortion-related mortality.	Provision of safe pregnancy termination, e.g. after rape on medical advice.
3 Reduction of harmful substance abuse.	Prohibitions on manufacture, advertising, distribution of cigarettes, alcohol, heroin plus derivatives. Taxing of tobacco and alcohol.
4 Reduction in road traffic deaths and injuries.	Minimum legal age for driving a vehicle. Restrictions on drinking and driving.
5 Access to prevention and early treatment for mental disorders.	Provision of services and home support for youths exposed to undue emotional and mental stress.
6 Avoidance of work-related accidents and injuries.	Prohibition of work in hazardous conditions or involving harmful chemicals.

Indirect policies and laws include: increasing access of girls to higher education/employment through schemes such as compulsory provision of places/scholarships, hostels for women, vocational training and job-placement schemes, minimum wages and equal pay; avoidance of work-related accidents and injuries; continuing education for pregnant adolescents; regulation of firearms and lethal weapons; and access to services and employment for disabled youth.

Stage 7 Adults (15–49 years)

1 Reduction in water-related diseases.	Compulsory sanitation for each dwelling/cluster, plus public drainage.
2 Food security for the poor.	Subsidy on staple cereal food-for-work programmes. Security of land rights for rural poor, especially women/widows.
3 Increase productive employment opportunities for disabled poor.	Compulsory recruitment of per centage of disabled in specified industries.
4 Increase access to reproductive health servicesincluding family planning/spacing for low-income groups.	Regulation of community-based contraceptive distributors.
5 Reduce health risks related to improper use of chemical fertilisers.	Regulation of use of chemical fertilisers.
6 Increase accessibility by poor livestock owners to animal health services.	Compulsory employment of animal health assistants at district level.
7 Protection of urban drinking water sources.	Regulation of industrial discharge practices.
8 Reduction of level of domestic violence against women.	Compulsory provision of legal aid for survivors of domestic violence.
9 Protection of widows.	Abolition of harmful mourning practices, e.g. widow becomes property of husband's brother. Change in inheritance law enabling widows to inherit land and property.
10 Increase access to health services for poor in malarious areas.	Regulation of practice for passive case detection by volunteer primary malaria workers.

| 11 | Avoidance of discrimination against HIV-infected people. | Penalties for employers who dismiss HIV-infected employees. |

Indirect policies and laws include: elimination of discriminatory employment practices such as bonded labour; organisation of labour unions; minimum wages; compulsory health and safety regulations for employers; agrarian reform; increased access to water for irrigation and other agricultural inputs; protection of community fishing rights; and non-formal education for indigenous and minority population.

Stage 8 Older people (50 and above)

1	Increase access to sheltered housing options for older people.	Subsidies for construction of low-cost sheltered housing/dwellings.
2	Increase in food security for older people who are refugees.	Compulsory food-for-work activities targeting older refugees.
3	Support older people who care for children orphaned through AIDS.	Compulsory home-care programmes at district level.
4	Increase security for older people who are disabled.	Pension or similar schemes supported by NGOs.

There needs to be clarity about how policies and laws will be implemented and by whom. The following example illustrates how refugee women became better protected through the action of lawyers and cooperation of the local police.

From Experience

In camps in northeast Kenya, home to over 100 000 Somalis, Ethiopian and Sudanese refugees, domestic violence, indecent assault, and rape of women and girls as young as six, formed the average monthly police caseload. A workshop supported by the United Nations Commission for Refugees (UNHCR) was organised by an all-women team of lawyers for local police who had gaps in their knowledge and practice of law. It focused on rights and needs of refugee women and children, and the role of police and others in their protection. Participants went through steps in prosecution of a rape case, international refugee law, key aspects of Kenyan law, improved methods of dealing with victims of violence and prevention of violent crime. From 29 reported rape cases monthly, over a year the incidence decreased to eight a month.

5.2 HOW CORRUPTION SABOTAGES PATHS OUT OF POVERTY

In development terms, corruption means the use of power for profit, preferment, prestige, or for the benefit of a group or class in a way that constitutes a breach of law, or standards of moral conduct. Corruption operates at various levels and overall produces a lethal cocktail designed to oppress the poor. The following examples are drawn from real experiences and show how corruption operates, often as a mainstream activity.

Levels at which corruption operates and examples of corruption

Conceptual or ideological

- Entrenched belief that the poor are inferior in human status to the non-poor. May be linked to attitudes of racial superiority

National practices

- Passing agrarian reform law but never implementing it.
- National elites regularly hijack funds/materials intended for development or for the poor, for example to build homes or open extra personal bank accounts.

- National teaching hospitals continue to absorb 20–60 per cent of total health budget.
- Leaders/political parties ignore unjust and exploitative social and labour practices, such as bonded labour.

Sub-national and provincial

- Non-operation or distortion of good welfare policies, such as when sick animals are given to a poor family for income generation.

District

- Parents obliged to give present to teacher to enrol secondary pupils.
- District managers spend money earmarked for health patrols on other purposes.
- Health staff only give care to in-patient if they receive money/food gifts.
- Public service drugs and medical instruments disappear, sold for profit privately.

- Development agencies know that elites hijack regular percentage of development aid, but accept the practice as part of price/hidden costs of development.

5.3 LINKS BETWEEN TOURISM, POVERTY AND HEALTH

Many countries rely on tourism as a major income earner. In 1992, some developing countries were receiving a million tourists a year, and others tens of thousands (with 200 million going to Europe annually). In 1995, there were estimated to be two and a half jumbo jets carrying holiday makers landing somewhere every minute of every day (Holden 1995).

Do the poor gain anything from other people's tourism?

What are the social consequences of tourism for people who are poor and vulnerable? Are there real financial and material advantages at community level? What part do communities play in determining growth or control of tourism in the areas where they live and work? What effect does tourism have on local leadership and community organisation patterns? How much traditional folklore is specially devised for tourists, and are traditional handicrafts being replaced by cheap souvenirs? Is there a 'coca-colonisation' taking place at the expense of local traditional values and patterns. Do local youths lured into tourism slide into alcoholism, drug taking and casual or commercial sex?

These questions are rarely asked and the social impact of tourism is rarely assessed. The poem 'The curtain of affluence' by Debbie Praphaphan (1968) admonishes the tourist:

'Look behind the curtain, and see what you shall see, not a land of paradise, but souls stripped of dignity. Children cry from hunger, women sell their souls for cash. Without a thought you buy our pride, like sidewalk souvenirs. Look behind the curtain tourist, maybe then you'll share our tears.'

How the poor are prostituted

Commercial sex is the flagship of many tourist promotions by low and middle-income countries. Even where prostitution is illegal, commercial sex is tolerated by government for fear of damaging the lucrative tourist industry. Even where local women are prevented by social and religious custom from being prostituted, policy hypocritically allows for the importation of foreign women as commercial sex workers. Sex tourism promotes traffic in women, international migration of women and mail-order brides. The women involved almost always come from among the poor and vulnerable groups.

Child prostitution has become a major social problem in countries in Asia and South America. Particularly affected in Asia are India, Thailand, Taiwan and the Philippines. In 1995 there were estimated to be over a million prostitutes under the age of 16 years in eight Asian countries. In

India, it was estimated that there were around 400 000 children involved in prostitution (Holden 1995). During the past two decades, specialist holiday tour operators in Europe, North America and Japan, and paedophile (adults who have sex with children) networks have become highly organised. The reports of its consequences are horrendous, like the twelve-year-old Filipino girl, Rosario, who arrived at hospital writhing in agony. She was found to have had a broken sex toy inside her uterus. Despite its removal she died.

Some concerned action groups and networks have managed to influence legislation in tourist-sending countries so that they can now prosecute citizens for offences committed against children overseas. Law is in place in Denmark, Finland, Norway, Iceland, Sweden, the USA, Belgium, France, Germany, Switzerland, Australia and New Zealand. Legislation is under way, or being considered by Italy, Canada, Iceland and the UK.

Other health consequences of tourism among the poor

Sex tourism is associated with sexually transmitted diseases and HIV infection, unwanted pregnancy and unsafe abortion. Local adolescents especially may not protect themselves from these diseases, for example by not using condoms. Women who are poor may not insist on condom use if they can get more money to feed their children by unprotected sex. With tourism comes the fast food industry and it is often the poorer people who tend to go for such foods, or be affected by changes brought about by tourism. For example, women who used to breastfeed find that employment allows no time for this and instead feed young children with fast foods as a replacement. Hotel managers find it easier to purchase fresh foods from supermarkets rather than local producers. Often, tinned foods are used.

But, there is still little control over tourism for the people who are directly affected by it. Communities need opportunities to define the shape that tourism should take within their own areas. People need to be able to stipulate boundaries, fair prices and certain standards with regard to behaviour of tourists (Holden 1995). There are examples of networks which are empowering people with information they need to protect themselves. For example, a string of hotels to be built in Indonesia would have displaced people and lost fishermen access to beaches but local people managed to delay opening of the last hotel to allow completion of negotiation with developers over access to the beach. Training workshops have been held to feed information on negative aspects of tourism to representatives of local people.

The next section continues the theme of policies and plans by focusing on a particular way in which the poor and vulnerable can participate in assessing their own needs, seeing what local policies are appropriate and making practical bottom-up plans for action against poverty and for health. In Chapter 2, ways were outlined for helping the poor to analyse and assess their own situations. The example which follows takes this a step further by involving them also in planning specific related actions at household and community level.

5.4 WHAT DOES A FAMILY NEED? – A PARTICIPATORY PLANNING EXERCISE

The following exercise has been carried out in various settings and in different cultures, including India, Papua New Guinea, Viet Nam and the Philippines. It has been found useful by rural villagers or urban poor families, and when training health workers.

Objectives of the exercise

The objective of the exercise 'What does a family need?' is to enable participants to rapidly create a visual profile of their basic needs as a basis for making local plans of action. In this way, they see a picture of what should be in place – but too often is not. They see what they themselves can provide, and what support is needed from others.

Steps in exercise (duration one to two hours)

1 Prepare a meeting place/room/school classroom with a blackboard and chalks, coloured if possible. (If the exercise is used during training, an overhead projector is useful (assuming there is electricity) and also a screen for projection of the images (sheet, cloth or suitable white or pale coloured wall). Prepare four to five clean overhead transparency sheets and water-based transparency markers in one to three colours if possible).

2 When the facilitator has created a comfortable and relaxed atmosphere the exercise begins. The facilitator asks: 'When you think of a family who do you think of first?' In some cultures the group will answer 'the mother' and in others 'the father'. The facilitator draws a circle and

adds eyes, nose, mouth, hair, according to whether it is the mother or father. Also, the facilitator draws simple female/male clothed body, for instance with skirt, sari, shirt, vest or sarong trousers. The audience usually watches with interest and sometimes amusement.

3 Next, the facilitator asks: 'What about the father/mother? Who can draw one?' Often people are shy to draw, unless they have some artistic ability, are schoolteachers, or are school children. But usually, with a little encouragement, people can be persuaded to draw a simple figure close to the one already drawn. The least artistic contributions often result in the most discussion and laughter.

4 The facilitator then asks: 'Who else is in the family?' Where there is an average of five or more children, several people/children can draw them (close to the mother and father, to leave plenty of space to later draw the family needs). Participants to draw children/toddlers/a baby as part of the family group.

5 The family is still not complete. The facilitator asks: 'What about the grandparents, or aunts/uncles/nephews living with the family?'. Again, participants are invited to draw them as part of the family group.

6 After ten minutes the extended family has been drawn in the middle of the blackboard. The facilitator remembers to praise the artists!

7 The facilitator says: 'Here is our family, but what does this family need?' This begins the process of identifying what a local family needs. One of the first needs usually mentioned by participants is food. A participant is invited to draw a simple symbol of the first, and perhaps all (to save time), of the family needs which are subsequently mentioned. Or the facilitator may draw them.

8 The next need mentioned is usually water, then land, money and education. Health may only be mentioned last! The facilitator/participants should only draw family needs mentioned by participants. If health is not mentioned, the facilitator can suggest a health need (for instance, relating to primary health care) at the end. The facilitator never provides answers, but instead stimulates/encourages participants to provide them, then adds a little.

9 The blackboard may eventually look something like the one on p. 98, which shows the results of the exercise among community representatives and health workers in India.

10 The facilitator then sums up what is on the blackboard, that is what the family needs. Then he/she asks: 'Which of these needs can the family obtain for themselves?' and encourages brief discussion on each of the needs drawn around the family. Some key questions may help to keep discussion focused, such as: 'How many families in this place/area do have safe drinking water? (Exact statistics are not required for the exercise because community members are unlikely to have them. However, health staff may have them).

11 The facilitator then encourages discussion of why some needs are absent, which can be obtained through local effort and which require

some assistance with technical/material/financial inputs from outside the community/neighbourhood. Perhaps poverty will not even be mentioned by name, but perhaps it will. Discussions about poverty can become very broad, leaving participants confused about appropriate local action. The facilitator can help by bringing the discussion back from time to time to focus on the family on the blackboard.

12 If time allows (or during an additional session), the facilitator can stimulate further analysis and discussion by asking 'How does money affect the needs drawn around the family?' and 'Which of these family needs are linked to each other?' The facilitator then draws the links between needs, such as between land and food, or health worker/care and immunisation of young children in the family.

13 At the end of the exercise the facilitator or a participant sums up the family needs in the area.

From Experience

In the poor, heavily populated state of Bihar, India, during a participatory evaluation of an urban and rural community health programme, health workers and community representatives identified what families needed. Their first needs were for food, water, shelter, land, money, employment, care for livestock, then education for children, electricity, and assets like bicycles. Only then came health care for women and children, and first aid. The facilitator helped them to include other health needs, such as immunisation against preventable childhood diseases, care for children with diarrhoea, care for mothers and newborn during pregnancy and childbirth, and family planning. A 'primary health care circle' emerged surrounding and protecting the family. (The illustration is more tidy than the original drawing by multiple 'artists'! Also identified during the exercise were simple 'indicators' or 'markers' by which local families and health workers could monitor their progress out of poverty and ill health.

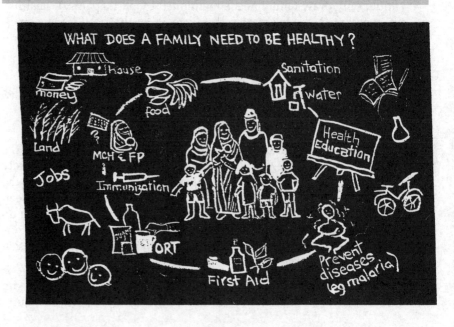

Poor people, and especially poor women, often have little initial self confidence in their own planning abilities. Bottom-up planning has been advocated for a long time, but does it really fit with more top-down planning?

5.5 AN UNEASY FIT – BOTTOM-UP WITH TOP-DOWN PLANNING

There is often lip service paid to bottom-up and participatory planning. Particularly in large projects/programmes, most major decisions of budgeting and time scale may already have been taken at the top before those at district/community level are involved. While this is partly understandable, it nevertheless tends to undermine the value of bottom-up planning. Participatory planning can take place at community, district, provincial and national level. Many of the principles are the same, but the participants, venue, time scale and materials used differ. For example, in Lesotho, national officials from ministries and local institutions and staff and consultants from UN agencies, used a rapid participatory planning method (using overhead projector and simple planning matrices) to produce in 12 days a practical two-year plan for safe motherhood for the whole country. Another example is the rapid participatory planning carried out in a province of Papua New Guinea where a team of provincial health officials with project staff from an integrated rural development project, using site visits, participatory problem analysis and a large whiteboard, developed over six weeks a detailed three-year action plan.

5.6 POLICY AND PLANNING – NGO PERSPECTIVES ON POVERTY AND HEALTH

Some successful NGO programmes originally began with very sketchy plans, if any. They originated and grew in response to urgent local problems. Over time, they introduced more systematic policy making, planning, monitoring and evaluation methods. There are wide variations among NGOs in terms of size, principles, attitudes, and management methods and recently, many NGOs have been analysing their own experiences. Many NGOs face financial and material shortages. They also often have to compete among themselves for such resources. Many NGOs are playing an important advocacy role at national and international level by drawing attention to the real conditions faced by people who are poor and vulnerable and the injustices which maintain them in that poverty.

Some problems faced during NGO policy making and planning

1   Instead of providing funding to NGOs, some governments and donors are tending towards contractual service agreements with them, say, for hospital services.

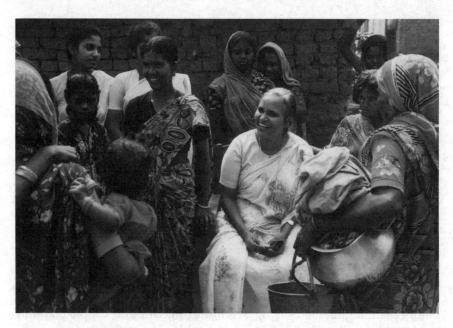

NGO staff in Bihar, India, planning action with lowest caste urban women.

2 NGOs may have to account to several parties (donors, government, communities and beneficiaries) and to manage conflicts between these parties.

3 At a time when NGO resources are shrinking, government services are diminishing and creating greater reliance on NGO services for help with, say, health and education.

4 An NGO wanting to adhere to principles of working for the benefit of the poor may find it difficult to retain a good working relationship with government. (Some governments have even withdrawn approval of support by foreign agencies for NGOs when they have disapproved of their policy stance.)

5 Striving to improve operations and to balance the books, NGOs can come in conflict with traditional free/low-cost help to the poor.

6 When donor funds are channelled to NGOs through government, time is wasted due to often heavy bureaucratic procedures.

7 Funds are given for too short a time scale to facilitate any difference at local level. Time needed to achieve sustainable changes at community/neighbourhood level is more than a couple of years.

8 The relationship between government and NGOs often seems unequal, weak, inconsistent and unsteady.

9 Governments often want NGO help, but are so inundated with their own problems that they have insufficient time to create a good working relationship.

10 More focal points are needed within government, specially for dealing with NGOs.

11 Governments allowing foreign NGOs to do direct community work in their countries can cause problems for existing local NGOs.

12 Many governments do not have clear policies and plans for eradicating poverty in situations where, for instance root causes include unequal land ownership.

13 Even if clear poverty eradication policies and plans exist, they may not be actively pursued if they clash with the interests of elites.

14 Without clear policies and strategies for poverty eradication, governments cannot indicate clear roles for NGOs in development. The overall framework is missing.

What kind of action is necessary for more effective government/NGO interactions ?

The following brief checklist can be useful in assessing how the situation is in a particular place:

- government is updating rules and legislation which governs NGOs
- a system has been established for registration of NGOs with a designated official national body
- there are 'umbrella' bodies which serve as gateways for NGO registration and access to funds
- an appropriate regulatory body exists which has equal representation on it from both NGOs and government
- a forum exists for regular government/NGO dialogue
- a mechanism exists for conflict resolution between governments and NGOs
- an NGO coalition exits to assist NGOs in evolving common positions, collective training approaches, mechanisms for self regulation and codes of conduct
- a code of ethics exists for NGOs and some form of accreditation of southern NGOs which would encourage northern NGOs to fund them
- southern NGOs have developed cooperative and joint programmes and collectively approach donors or funding
- southern NGOs know the terms on which northern NGOs obtain funds for them
- changes of policy or objectives are not made by the northern NGOs without the agreement of their southern partners
- NGOs have access to information on policy issues relevant to their work in the field of poverty.

(Adapted from Commonwealth Foundation (1995a).)

Lack of money and credit are major obstacles to the poor in trying to raise themselves out of poverty.

5.7 PLANNING FINANCIAL SERVICES AND CREDIT FOR THE POOR

There has been a common misconception that people who are poor cannot handle money effectively and do not know how to save, and that women are credit risks. But growing evidence confirms that this is not the case. For example, a study in Bangladesh found that programmes which focus on women have higher repayment rates than traditional credit schemes which have excluded women. Also, the large-scale Grameen Bank scheme for the poor of Bangladesh boasted a 98 per cent loan repayment rate and had an 84 per cent female membership. Financial managers purposely targeted women borrowers because they were more disciplined and more careful with capital. Nevertheless, it is still difficult in many places for the poor to get access to financial services and credit schemes.

People who are poor often need small scale finance, as their activities are often small scale, such as garment and cottage industries. Helping small-scale savers and borrowers to get money can raise their productivity and incomes. Without money, small businesses must wait before they can purchase materials, resulting in inefficiency and disruption in production. They cannot take advantage of discounts on raw materials. To obtain enough cash to meet daily expenses, they must sell goods immediately – even if market prices are not favourable. Women in agriculture commonly need credit in the planting season. There are informal and semi formal financial services for the poor.

Informal financial services and credit for the poor

Community banks (also known as revolving systems for credit and savings (ROSCAs))

These are community groups which meet regularly to agree loans from a shared fund and to make savings and repayments. The group usually selects a committee, and funds may be provided by a donor. The committee decides who is eligible for a loan, what amount it should be, conditions of repayment and the interest charge. Members may be encouraged to make savings at the same time as repayments and these are kept in a separate account. If any member fails to repay, other members of the bank are responsible for them. The cycle of loans and repayments may continue for five years, though members can drop out of the scheme if they wish. Savings are used as individuals wish, including intestment to help continue the community bank. In Honduras, Central America, a women's community bank system had 113 banks in 1994, with 4000 members. At weekly meetings the women also learnt about nutrition, health, literacy and Bible studies. Some ROSCAs also have a special loan fund that is lent out, or given as grants, to needy members.

Solidarity groups

These are similar to the community bank, except that people who want to borrow are encouraged to form 'solidarity' groups where members guarantee each other's loans. In Guatemala, Central America, a solidarity bank is helping groups of farmers escape the exploitation of wealthy farmers who traditionally bought all crops at harvest time when prices were low, selling them later once prices rise. Now farmers do not immediately have to sell their harvested crops, but store them and sell later for a better price. They then repay the loan and enjoy increased income.

Individual loans

Individuals provide security for the loan, such as land or machinery, which can be resold if the loan is not paid. For example, a farmer may want to buy a water pump to increase his agricultural output, or a health worker in a remote location may want to take a loan to buy a set of medical instruments so that they can provide better care to the community. Individual loans also include those provided by family and friends in time of need. They may also be provided by professional money lenders and pawnbrokers, tradespeople and money collectors.

Solving the collateral problem

It can be a major problem for the poor to get a loan if they do not have assets to serve as collateral against the loan. But experiences indicate that there are innovative ways around even this problem.

Generally, informal financial service agents know their clients better than formal bank staff do. This reduces their information costs and lowers staff and administration costs. Their interest rates are not regulated so they can adjust to market forces. But they have their limits too, such as not being able to provide large loans. They have difficulty coping with inflation and

In 1994 a Christian-based development group operating in Bangladesh for 20 years decided to start lending to the poor – without any security. The poor were too poor to have any assets. The maximum they could have saved was $5 over two years, or a group of 20 could save $100 in two years. It was too long to wait. By 1996 there was a well-organised credit and loan scheme with over 7000 members, and a revolving fund loan of $150 000. With loans of between $10–15 people began projects to dry fish, sell kerosene, vegetables and fish, knit fishnets, rear goats and poultry, make paper bags and knit garments. Loans of between $50–200 were used to sell cloth, kitchen equipment and fertiliser, for weaving, making and selling sweets, to buy a bullock for ploughing, a sewing machine or loom, to produce molasses from sugar cane or set up a small shop. Larger loans, only available to those who repaid loans, were used for buying knitting machines, power pumps, rice mills, soap factories, ice factories, rickshaws and carts, or to set up poultry farms, fish ponds and tailoring shops.

The loan repayment rate is over 97 per cent. There is an annual service charge of 12 per cent. Of this, two per cent goes to a welfare fund, which is used to partially pay any unpaid loan (the rest being recovered from members' savings account), or to cover repayments if a member dies with no heir to repay the loan, leaves the area suddenly, suffers a natural disaster, or becomes physically or mentally ill. Training is provided to the groups. The scheme has enabled the poor to avoid money lenders, save money themselves, increase women's confidence and has indirectly resulted in improved health and schooling for children.

it is said that, as long as poor people rely on informal financial markets, they will remain outside the economic mainstream.

Semi-formal financial services for the poor

Developed mainly over the past 15 years, these vary in size, ownership and organisation. They include the *innovative commercial banks* which specialise in financial programmes, such as a government-owned bank in Indonesia which tries to combine commercial and social banking objectives. In the People's Bank of Nigeria scheme, vulnerable rural women who accessed credit increased their income from $25 to $180 in only 18 months, and in urban areas their income increased from $465 to $1000 in 12 months (WHO 1994c). Then there are *financial intermediaries*, commonly NGOs such as Women's World Banking, or government agencies who channel credit from banks to small borrowers. They also provide training, referrals, help with loan applications and guarantees to lenders which reduce transaction costs to both borrowers and lenders. Some women's banks lend as little as $50. Lending $10 000 to one person results in lower administrative costs than lending 200 people $50 each. But costs of promoting the scheme have to be met by the scheme itself – unless voluntary work is contributed and the scheme receives contributions in kind.

There are also *parallel programmes*, institutions (usually NGOs), set up to provide financial services to the poor outside the formal financial sector. For example, in Cameroon, Africa, there is the Cooperative Credit Union League, while Zimbabwe has the Savings and Development Foundation, and in Madras, India, they have the Working Women's Forum.

There are also the better known *poverty-oriented development banks* which combine grassroots development and financial services. For example, the Grameen Bank in Bangladesh and the People's Bank in Nigeria organise their members into groups and press for social development, in addition to providing financial services. Using this model, the Grameen Bank has reached more than 800 000 people, mostly women. The People's Bank of Nigeria has reached about 700 000 people, and in 1994, it had a loan recovery rate of around 98 per cent. A similar type of bank in Indonesia which deals in larger credit reached about 2.7 million people in 1982. It does not organise groups, but works with local leaders, such as mayors, to get references and identify poorer members of the community. One country may need several types of such financial services schemes operating at different levels to meet the needs of small-scale savers and borrowers.

5.8 LINKS BETWEEN WOMEN'S INCREASED INCOME AND IMPROVED FAMILY HEALTH

Increasing income for women often has better outcomes for family health than increasing income for men. For example, men who are poor may be more likely to spend money on alcohol and cigarettes, while women are more likely to spend it on food. In the Solomon Islands, women are turning seeds into money thanks to a credit scheme. An urban-based women's group needed cash income to cope with family feeding, clothing, housing and paying school fees. They started a 'sup-sup' (mixed) Garden Credit Union. Seeds were provided by a cooperative. Money raised was lodged with Credit Union and loans were then available for the families. Other group activities included catering for workshops and business gatherings. Workshops were run on better gardening and child nutrition, and benefits could be seen in improved child health (Hata 1996).

In the context of policy making and planning, the poor seem sometimes to be treated as objects or statistics. The next chapter looks at what it feels like to be poor drawing on the experiences of the poor themselves.

WHAT DOES IT FEEL LIKE TO BE POOR?

This chapter looks inside poverty. What does being poor actually mean in the life of a person/family who is poor? How does it affect their opportunities, their day-to-day living and their escape routes from poverty? Why are people who are poor so often treated as objects, and what does this do to their self esteem? What do the poor do to help themselves? Some misconceptions about the poor are explored.

The chapter then considers what are the main assets of the poor, and whether they can hold on to them. What happens when they lose them? Why are women dispoportionately affected by poverty and how does this relate to their health? Some actions are suggested against increasing feminisation of poverty.

6.1 PSYCHOLOGICAL ASPECTS OF POVERTY

Many studies have focused on the physical aspects of poverty and health, such as weighing and measuring poor children, the assets of the poor, or amount of income generated in relation to costs of basic commodities. There has been more interest in the physical and social problems of the poor than of their psychological, emotional or spiritual state. It was presumed, perhaps, that attention to basic material needs would change or solve psychological aspects of poverty. But this is only partly correct. There is increasing evidence of mental disorders among the poor (in western industrialised countries too). There is also a continuing tendency to treat the poor and vulnerable differently to the non-poor. This is deeply resented by people who are poor and contributes to their frequent feelings of inferiority and lack of self-esteem.

From Experience

It is nine o'clock on Saturday morning. The clinic is in full swing. The man sits alone amid a crowd of waiting patients, head bent towards the ground. He appears about 60 years old. Looking haggard and desolate and in a tremendous amount of pain, he glances towards the doctor in fear, hope, and sheer desperation. He had tried to get help from many places, but none were able or willing to admit him. The covering on his head, a dirty orange rag, is removed by the doctor. The man avoids eye contact as the unbearable stench, almost choking, is released. At the very top of his head, having eaten through the scalp, are two big cavities, separated by a bridge of skin. Both are filled to the brim with pus and infection. His hair and beard are crawling with lice.

The man's medical history revealed a fall two weeks before. In the rundown bustee where he lives without sanitation, it was difficult to keep it clean. We take him to a dressing area. Giving time for the painkiller to take effect, the task of cleaning his horribly infected wound is begun. Bit by bit the cleaning continues for an hour. We stop to give him a break. He looks up and says: 'Two hundred – you have removed the two hundredth maggot from my head'. He has been counting these wriggling pests as they are pulled out with forceps and dropped on the plate.

After another 38 maggots, the pus and dirt also removed, healthy pink tissue can be seen underneath. The procedure is completed in two hours, the whole area cleaned, packed and covered with a clean white dressing. Conversation has been at a bare mininimum the entire time. How he must have felt cannot be described. The dressing finally completed, the man stands up and stumbles towards the dressings table. He falls to his knees, his hands tightly clasped. He is praying. This moment I will never forget. A few minutes later he stands again, looks around and starts to thank us all with warm and genuine affection. We organise antibiotics, painkillers, clean clothes and some food for him to take home. One hour later he is still standing by the dressings area. He has, despite his haggard look, a beautiful smile. Back the next day, he is a changed man. With his beard shaved and a change of clothes he looks a generation younger. He is, in fact, 35 years old.

(E. O'Sullivan, of the Valentia Hospital, Kerry Ireland.)

6.2 WHY ARE POOR PEOPLE SO OFTEN TREATED AS OBJECTS?

Are poor people treated as objects because they are regarded as inferior? In some cultures this is how they are regarded. Is it because the poor may not appear be as articulate as the non-poor (they may not express themselves so clearly, or they may not be literate)? Is it because, with the material and economic obsessions of the eighties and nineties, being poor is seen as being at the lowest level of society? Is it because those who are in more frequent contact with the poor either have little patience with them or little time for them? In the example from India on page 107, busy health staff only gradually became aware of what a poor man really felt as he was treated.

6.3 SHARING THE PAIN OF POVERTY

Those who are poor sometimes speak of the 'pain' of poverty. What does this consist of? What do the poor and vulnerable feel? Is it any different from what those who are not poor would feel, were they to exchange places? Sometimes those who work closely with the poor and vulnerable come to share their pain; some are even killed for sharing it. Gains in the struggle for social justice and opportunities for the poor to lift themselves out of poverty and reduce vulnerability are sometimes short lived. Some are small and loosely organised, like local protest marches, others are more extensively organised.

From Experience

In Chiapas, southern Mexico, a peasant uprising by the Zapatista National Liberation Army (EZLN) was symbolically launched in 1994. This insurrection, described as 'one of the most unexpected, brilliantly staged peasant uprisings in living memory' (Hernandez 1994) lasted only four days, until the Mexican army drove the rebels back into the mountains. Indian villages were bombed and destroyed.

Seventy per cent of Mexico's population and much of the national media sided with the rebels. Their demand was for land rights for small farmers, fair and democratic elections, honest implementation of agrarian reform, a minimum wage high enough for poor people to adequately feed their children, an end to institutionalised corruption and graft, and to discrimination against indigenous people and the poor. They made it clear they did not want to overturn the government, but they wanted to clean it up and make it more representative and accountable to the people. Fearing a national revolt, or political repercussions, the army was called off and many of the peasant demands met. At the bargaining table the president offered pardon to the rebels if they gave up their weapons. The rebel leader replied:

Why do we have to be pardoned?
What are we going to be pardoned for?
For not dying of hunger?
For not being silent in our misery?
For not accepting our historic role?
Of being despised and outcast?

For carrying guns into battle
Rather than bows and arrows?
For being Mexicans?
For being indigenous peoples?
For having called on the people of Mexico
To struggle for what belongs to them?
For having fought for liberty, democracy
and justice?
For not giving up?
For not selling out?
Who must ask for pardon?
And who must grant it?
Those who for years
Have satisfied themselves at full tables
While death sat beside us so regularly
That we finally stopped
Being afraid of it?
Or, should we ask pardon
From the dead,
Those who died 'natural' deaths
from 'natural' causes
Like measles, whooping cough,
Dengue, cholera, typhoid
Malaria and other diseases?
Our dead – the democratically dead
Dying from sorrow
Because nobody did anything.
Because the dead, our dead
Went just like that,
Without even counting them.
Without anyone saying
ENOUGH
Which would at least
Have given some meaning
To their deaths.
A meaning that no one
Ever sought for them
The forever dead
Who are now dying again
But this time
In order to live.

6.4 THE POOR, POLITICAL POWER AND THE LAW

How many times have politicians sought the votes of the poor, promising many reforms and benefits? How many times have those electoral promises been broken after succesful election? In some places the poor may believe to some extent in political pre-election promises. In others, they are cynically resigned to the fact that no benefits have resulted from their votes.

Generally, local people/households who are poor have little access to legal assistance when they need it. Legal advice and legal services are minimally developed for the poor and vulnerable. Their opportunities for redress of just grievances may only be through traditional means, such as taking vengeance by family/extended family. Linked to lack of access to legal advice and services is lack of confidence in law enforcement officers. The relationship between the poor and the police in many places is very poor. The police are rarely seen as on the side of the poor. Rather, they are seen as on the side of the powerful, wealthy, landowning elites and local criminal gangs which control drug trafficking and prostitution. Not infrequently, high political links can be traced in some of these activities, serving to protect corrupt police against the wellbeing of those who are too poor to resist the oppression.

For the non-poor sections of a population, the poor are often seen as a burden, a brake on progress, or a threat to stability. The non-poor have various beliefs and attitudes towards the poor. There may also be misconceptions about the poor.

6.5 THE POOR ARE NOT IDLE – THEY WORK

It is a major misconception to speak of the 'idle poor' in developing countries. For example, rural poor farmers, herders and fishermen are in reality poor producers. Their incomes are gained from their work. The answer to poverty lies in creating the conditions for people to earn more from their work. The poor are not idle, they work to survive. Too often in the past, poverty alleviation has been seen as a burden on the economy, as involving transfer of something to nothing in exchange. Instead, it should be seen as an investment in production, so if poverty can be defined as a production problem, poverty alleviation as can be seen as an investment (IFAD 1994).

6.6 THE MAIN MATERIAL ASSETS OF THE POOR

What is an asset? The exact meaning is 'property available to meet debts'. It also means any possession, which can be a person or thing, having any useful quality. What are the main assets owned by the poor? In rural areas the poor may own very few non-fixed assets (their fixed assets being their shelter). Their personal property may consist of basic clothes, cooking utensils, food serving dishes and utensils, thin blankets, woven items (baskets/bags, food carriers, seives and grain winnowers), hand-made agricultural tools, water containers (pottery, brass, tin, bamboo) and a storage container (trunk, case, box, woven container) to keep valued family items in. The very poor rarely own watches, radios or bicycles. In countries where dowry practice is common, women may have items of jewellery and special festive clothing.

In Honduras, Central America, the season's maize cobs are stored close to the adobe (mud-plastered) dwellings of poor farmers. They are piled up, under cover, next to the front entrance. This is equivalent to keeping a close eye on the assets. In the poorest homes in India, special carefully crafted and mud-plastered grain storage bins are constructed inside the homes by the women. The precious grain is then sealed inside the cool storage bin, with only one tap exit left low down in the plastered surface. This prevents access by grain-destroying insects and rodents. Livestock such as chickens, pigs, goats and cattle are guarded from thieves and predators. They are the riches of the poor. The poor do not have banks in which to guard their material assets, such as jewellery.

Marketing material assets

In many places, production and use of local artifacts like water containers, baskets and pottery, have altered a great deal in response to market forces and modernisation. Indigenous production methods and patterns have often been altered to produce items which will sell better – which are more marketable. Whereas each pattern migh once have had a symbolic significance, modern items may jumble up a range of patterns, resulting in no message, or very mixed messages. It may be good for business, but it has degraded some indigenous characteristics which have often been cherished by the poor.

6.7 THE VULNERABLE HUMAN ASSETS OF THE POOR

Poor families traditionally have many children to provide labour in the fields and factories or on the streets. These human assets become part of the pattern of survival and debt repayment. The most notorious system of using human assets was slavery and indentured labour (see Chapter 2), and the latter is extensively used in pursuit of economic gain. A close relative is 'bonded' labour. In this system, whole families are endlessly bonded to landowners or industrial producers, in a cycle of debt and deprivation. Their labour or produce is never quite enough to repay their debt to the boss. The next generation is still enslaved under the guise of debt repayment. In some places, a landlord can still command the first night of the virginal bride of a male bonded labourer; the ultimate in slavery and degradation. In very many places, there are elites and so-called developed people who practice a minor form of 'slavery' through minimally paid servants, usually female.

Problems arise as the poor want – and need – to exploit their human assets. For example, in the Americas and Asia, some poor families send their young daughters to work ostensibly as domestic employees and factory workers, but in reality they often become prostitutes. The money they send home used to buy basic items such as food and clothing, and pay for the school fees of younger siblings. But now, in some places the money is used to buy items such as televisions and even video players. The young girls often return to their villages with HIV infection.

6.8 THE TRADE IN HUMAN ORGANS

People who are poor not only sell their whole bodies, but they may sell parts of their bodies. For example, the seller of a kidney in India is almost always poor and understands little about the personal effect of removing such a vital organ – even if he/she has another left. Middle men may take part of the payment from a transplant team and are unlikely to pass on more than a token amount to the donor of an irreplaceable organ. What is the fair price for a human kidney? Unrelated live donors are being used for kidney transplants.

Only the poor will make such a sacrifice for the sake of money, and only the rich can afford to buy. People who are rich and do not have a related donor are reluctant to accept an organ from a dead person: 'Why should I take a diseased kidney from a dead person,' they might ask, 'when I can buy a healthy man's kidney?' The poor are usually less educated and cannot comprehend the risks involved (kidney donors can die later). There have been donors who developed disease in their remaining kidney, years after their donation. If the kidney donor is related to the family, the support of the family may be forthcoming, but for the unrelated donor, there is no such connection and the sick donor often dies in poverty.

Besides the voluntary sale by the poor of their body organs, there is also the involuntary use of their organs and body parts.

Illegal trade in human organs – the poor even pay with their lives

A wall of silence surrounds this trade. It involves corrupt doctors, surgeons, politicians and a web of buyers and sellers. Many developing countries supply human organs to richer countries, as there is a great demand for such organs and large sums may be paid due to their scarcity. For example, an American human rights activist claims that 20 000 people in the USA are waiting for transplants, and that annually around 4000 organ transplants are carried out (CIMADE 1996). But this is estimated to be more than the official organ suppliers could produce, so where are the other organs coming from? Private clinics are reported to have links with foreign suppliers.

On the US–Mexican border children and illegal immigrants are reported to be particularly vulnerable to the trade in human organs. Children have disappeared. Their families do not know if they were abducted for prostitution or their organs. The price of a kidney in the border town was reported to be US$15 000 (quoted by a doctor), yet Mexican officials claim there is no trade in human organs. That town, like other slum areas in South America, contains many ophthalmologists – in excess of what the population might need. The poor themselves cannot afford them, so for whom are they working? There might be a clue somewhere in the fact that a pair of corneas can generate US$6000 for the trafficker.

In 1992, a group of 60 poor families whose children had disappeared formed a foundation to publicise their fears. One missing child was subsequently found dead, with a kidney removed. Others have not been traced. The police are reported to be more interested in other problems, like drug trafficking. Abduction of children in Mexico is only a common law offence, and this means that no proceeding can be taken against other states.

Mental patients robbed of their corneas

In Argentina, human rights activists drew attention to a psychiatric institution where up to a thousand patients had disappeared. Families were told that patients had 'left voluntarily', but some had been too disabled to move easily by themselves. Then there was evidence that some patients had been killed. Some graves were exhumed, and corpses were found whose eye-balls had been removed. Furthermore, one 26-year-old survivor who had entered the hospital sighted emerged a year later, blind. Both corneas had been removed surgically. The hospital director was replaced as the scandal emerged.

> ### From Experience
> In Colombia, human rights activists drew attention to an institution housing hundreds of blind children. The cause of blindness in some children was not clear. There were also disturbing reports of infants born sighted who had been hospitalised elsewhere – and who later emerged blind. One mother claimed: 'My son went in with acute diarrhoea. They gave him back to me with bandages around his head. He had no eyes.' His dossier was later found to have been burnt. Another mother was given US$20 after her child emerged blinded. Ophthalmologists report that corneas are exported from the country and that there are informal agreements with foreign cornea banks.
>
> One of many poor people who make a living from collecting rubbish was lured by the promise of old cardboard boxes into an attack, during which he was shot and wounded and feigned death. He was taken to a morgue full of corpses. Many were without heads or limbs and some had had their internal organs removed. None still had eyes. This morgue was linked to a university.

The real extent of the trade in human organs is not known. How could it be when patients' notes and dossiers in developing countries mysteriously disappear? In some places, however, evidence does exist, such as medical reports and payment cheques for human organs. Human rights activists and journalists who have tried to expose this problem have been threat-ened and even had their homes bombed. The few investigations tried have come to nothing, dashed against a wall of silence to protect high-level vested interests. For example, countries that receive human organs do not want their reputations soiled, while in countries which provide organs, political, financial and professional pressures combine to hinder the course of justice to stop this obscene trade. In the South it is said that the eyes of northern countries seem to be closed to this trade.

| This wall of silence is a wall of shame. |

The blood trade – highlighted by the advent of AIDS

The whole question of people who are poor selling their blood was high-lighted with the advent of the HIV virus which causes AIDS. When it was realised that blood and blood products can carry the virus, transmitting it to those who receive the blood or products made from blood, a major global initiative was organised (coordinated by WHO's Global Programme on Aids). This initiative planned to assist countries to ensure that all blood donated/obtained from paid donors was free of HIV and other disease-causing elements, such as the virus causing hepatitis.

In some developing countries there remains a flourishing blood trade, where people who are poor sell their blood to raise money. This has been described in the Americas as 'squeezing blood from young people in the slums'. Many of these paid blood donors live in poor conditions and are in poor health, yet the people who are forced to sell their blood in this way are precisely those who would be unable to buy it should they need blood transfusion. For example, commerial blood donors in India are mainly young, illiterate males who are pavement dwellers, most of them separated from family and often addicted to alcohol or drugs (Feuerstein 1993b).

FILL IN THE PRICE TAGS - IF YOU KNOW THE PRICE--

From Experience
The illustration shows just what the poor are being forced to sell – and at what price. Unfortunately, there are middle men and others who cream off part of the profits. Often the poor – whose bodies or body parts are being sold – receive relatively little from the sale of such human assets.

6.9 WHEN THE POOR LOSE THEIR ASSETS

The poor may lose their assets gradually – or quickly. If some assets are sold off from time to time, as when the harvest has been poor and cannot provide food for the whole season, the poor may gradually have to sell their assets. However, if illness strikes, the costs of medicines or surgery may force the poor to sell assets rapidly, and with dire consequences. If a natural disaster such as a flood, typhoon or earthquake occurs, the poor may lose their assets instantly, with no benefit from their departure. If a man-made disaster such as war creates the need for the poor to flee and become refugees, they may lose their assets instantly. The poor are not insured; their losses are often absolute.

6.10 SEEING THE LINKS IN SURVIVAL PATTERNS

In the last chapter we saw how people who are poor often have little confidence in their own planning abilities. This may be due to low self esteem, or lack of literacy and numeracy skills. But there are other factors which must also be considered. Sometimes, those who visit poor communities are so heavily influenced by their own preconceptions of development, that they only notice its lack. It has been observed generally that 'they see only what is not there'. They have difficulty in seeing what *is* there, and do not easily appreciate subtle links between the patterns and artifacts of survival. For example, new water pumps are introduced with little training for maintenance and little provision for acquiring spare parts.

New cooking methods are advocated which necessitate the purchase of ovens or cooking utensils. Most devastating is where new patterns of agricultural or livestock production are introduced, with little success, but which undermine previous survival patterns. The poor are often accused of being cautious, even reluctant, to try changes. The truth is that they can ill afford to risk the consequences of a failed innovation.

For a development agency/extension service, a failed innovation may be quietly shelved. It is the poor communities themselves who are left with the trailing ends of ruptured survival patterns which had previously sustained their ancestors through hostile circumstances.

6.11 HOW POVERTY AFFECTS FAMILY LIFE

The strain of survival in hostile circumstances can be a degrading and weakening process, as parents see even their extensive efforts are not preventing the premature deaths or increasing malnutrition of their young children. The strain of unplanned and unspaced pregnancies also exerts an inhuman toll in such circumstances, leading too many poor people to resort to unsafe abortion. Hospitals and mortuaries are full of women who are/were poor and pregnant. Previous traditions of caring for the older family members, those who are disabled and those who are seeking work in a city are being weakened considerably in many places as families are hit by poverty – or sink into deeper poverty. Such supportive functions used to mitigate some of the effects of being poor, but people are being left increasingly more vulnerable.

The Year of the Family (1994) highlighted the function and the contemporary plight of the family. For people who are poor, having a functioning family system of some kind can increase survival margins. For example, a rural family which can feed itself can still care for older family members as it has always done. An urban 'family' of youths who live and work on the streets has better survival potential for its members than isolated members. Among the families most at risk are single-parent families, households headed by widows (who may be older persons) and households headed by women.

6.12 FIGHTING THE INCREASING FEMINISATION OF POVERTY

This section of the chapter looks at some specific types of action against poverty and for health which can reduce the feminisation of poverty. Perhaps one day it may even contribute to eliminating it.

Action for income generation and access to credit and loans

Increased action is needed in designing income-generating and credit schemes according to the realities and needs of poor and vulnerable women. This includes providing extension services and credit to women farmers, and involving them in better ways of managing natural resources. In urban areas it involves providing employment opportunities for women, and training them to manage water projects, including schemes through which they can form women's associations which sell water.

Action for appropriate education

Increased action is needed in: improving access of girls who are poor to basic education, increasing the number of female teachers and making the curriculum more relevant to the needs of poor households. (Some examples of innovative ways of reaching the unreached are outlined in Chapter 4.) As well as primary education, more appropriate secondary education and vocational opportunities can do much to strengthen the opportunities of girls from poor backgrounds who manage to reach that level. Some existing types of education of this type are divorced from the practical realities of poverty as currently existing.

Action to provide opportunities for fertility control

Action is needed to improve access of poor and vulnerable women and their husbands/partners to approaches and methods through which they can plan and space their children. This includes training community-based contraceptive distributors and making a wider choice of contraceptive methods, including natural family planning, available in the right place, at the right time and at the right cost. It also includes setting up ways in which those who use contraceptives/natural family planning can have access to advice, treatment and follow-up care when they need it.

Action for women's health, including safe motherhood

Action for women's health includes paying particular attention to nutritional status and the needs of poor and vulnerable girls and women. It means attention to their nutritional requirements during growth, youth, adolescence and the reproductive period (15–49 years). This may involve extension services for improved food production, accessibility to nutrition advice and guidance, and improved cooking, food processing and storage methods. It may include methods of accessing good quality, better-priced food, for instance through fair-price shops. Attention is needed to nutrition and health requirements during pregnancy, delivery, after the birth, during lactation and between pregnancies. Some current methods of dealing with these aspects are still very fragmented and not intersectoral. Such action must, of course, be closely linked with development of action for improved care for newborn infants and young children of poor and vulnerable women.

6.13 Ill health undermines survival chances

Chronic illness can be particularly devastating for those who are poor. Unlike an acute illness, which may also project a family below the poverty line or into deeper poverty, chronic illness just takes longer as it relentlessly saps family energy and erodes survival chances. In Chapter 3, some links between HIV infection and poverty are traced, as well as the outcomes. There is also the burden of seeing a family member/partner suffering with little recourse to assistance, and there can be a feeling of extreme powerlessness among carers.

Being sick undermines the productive capacity of those who are poor. A sick woman cannot plant and harvest food crops or fetch water. A sick unskilled male worker cannot migrate in search of employment in a mine or factory. Instead of being a productive asset sick people become unproductive liabilities. Yet, the degree of sickness under which a poor person still continues to work is often very different to that of western industrialised countries. For example, having a fever is rarely excuse enough not to engage in agricultural or domestic work. Even women who are heavily pregnant can be seen working in the fields until practically the moment of delivery, in many primary schools there are always children who are not well but continue to attend classes.

So, what DOES it feel like to be poor? Those who suffer poverty and deprivations often feel less equal to other people. They feel low self esteem and have less confidence in their own abilities to change their situation. They feel more at the mercy of fate and destiny. If they do not form part of an extended family or community, they feel loneliness and vulnerability. They feel little power to help dependants, young or old. Without a welfare system they are forced to rely on the goodwill of others – which may be variable and in short supply. They are more exposed to violence. Being poor is difficult enough, but being unhealthy or sick as well decreases survival chances radically. It undermines productivity, turning human assets into liabilities. It destroys the likelihood of escaping from poverty; it cuts off the escape routes from poverty.

Participatory approaches release and channel the energies of poor women to create their own paths out of poverty.

> **Ill health cuts escape routes from poverty**

ENVIRONMENT, HEALTH AND POVERTY

How do natural and man-made environments affect the health and lives of people who are poor? This chapter begins by looking at factors combining to damage the natural environment, including over-rapid population growth, and urbanisation. The meaning of more sustainable development is explored, especially as it affects the air, land, food production, forests, wildlife, fresh water, and ocean and fishery resources on which the livelihood and wellbeing of the poor often depend. Extraction of minerals and metals, and generation of certain types of energy also have implications for the health and lives of the poor. There are some practical suggestions for participatory assessment and action to protect the local environment at the same time as protecting human health. The next focus is on environments of conflict and violence, and what happens when the poor are forced to flee as 'eco-refugees' when the environment degrades.

7.1 THE NATURAL ENVIRONMENT AND HOW IT IS BEING DAMAGED

Both natural and man-made environments affect poverty and health. What is happening to the natural environment? Signs of environmental stress are growing. For example, there are worn-out farmlands, eroded hillsides, polluted water, parched and burnt grasslands, smoke-laden air, a depleted ozone layer in the atmosphere and treeless ranges. Each year, about 17 million hectares of tropical forest vanish – an area the size of Tunisia or Uruguay. The lakes, rivers and seas have in many places been over fished and/or polluted, and their rich harvests decimated. Dams and roads have sometimes been constructed with little thought of their environmental impact. Water, instead of sustaining life, is causing disease as industrial and other wastes are discharged into rivers and seas. The air is polluted with harmful substances and cities are clogged with rubbish (*Population Reports* 1992).

The illustration What Happens To Rubbish? shows how damaging rubbish can be to the natural environment. It has been adapted, with permission, from Tear Fund (1994).

WHAT HAPPENS TO THE RUBBISH ?

NEWSPAPER
Usually takes just a few weeks to decay.

CARDBOARD BOXES
Can take several months to decay.

BANANA LEAVES
Usually take just a few weeks to decay. Make compost from such waste materials.

LEATHER SHOES
Can take up to 50 years to decay.

THIN PLASTIC
Like food wrappings, can take up to five years to decay.

PLASTIC BAGS
Like that used for bread bags takes 10–20years to decay.

ALUMINIUM DRINK CANS
Can take up to 80 years to decay. Try using them as pots for seedlings.

PLASTIC RINGS
Like those holding beer and drink cans together can take up to 100 years to decay.

SCRAP METALS
May take up to 50 years to decay, depending on metal.

TYRES
Many uses so rarely seen as rubbish, but take so long to break down that no figure yet available!

PLASTIC BOTTLES
Most kinds will last indefinitely, but scientists developing type capable of eventually breaking down in sunlight.

GLASS BOTTLES
Usually reused or recycled, but once broken can take up to a million years to decay. They erode like rock.

PESTICIDE CONTAINERS
Are dangerous, never leave lying around, clean in river for reuse or burn. Always dispose in special rubbish pits. Same for old batteries which contain dangerous chemicals.

The problem of human numbers and human needs

The world's human population may continue to grow by more than 90 million each year. Each of these people needs a portion of the earth's resources for food, shelter, energy and water. The United Nations Fund for Population Activities (UNFPA) estimates that world population could reach six billion by the year 2001, and that around 95 per cent of growth will occur in developing countries. When a population is small and scattered, soils and forests can replenish themselves over time. As population density increases, more pressures are put on the land to grow food and produce fuel wood. Intensive cultivation results in several harvests wrung from the same area of land in quick succession, not allowing the land time to recuperate. Fragile areas, those with poor soils, erratic rainfall or hilly terrain, which previously supported small numbers of people, have been destroyed by intensive farming. Land which was traditionally watered (wetlands) has been filled in, destroying places where wild birds and animals once roamed.

7.2 IS THE GROANING PLANET REACHING ITS THRESHOLD?

As the global population grows and rapacious consumption patterns continue, we are beginning to see nature's limits. The natural ecosystems (ecological systems) are not having an opportunity to recover and renew themselves, or to absorb wastes. A *threshold effect* – a point of no return – may occur. For example, a lake can absorb a certain amount of pollutants without being harmed. But as the amount increases, a threshold is eventually reached, beyond which it cannot cope. It becomes unable to produce food or absorb any further pollutants. Fish become poisoned and die. Eventually the lake itself dies, becoming a stretch of dead water in which no fish or plants can live, and from which humans and animals cannot drink. A whole ecosystem has been killed, one which had probably been there for millions of years.

The planet is groaning under its increasing burden. Three main factors combine to determine the effect of human society on the environment:
- the number of people
- the average individual's level of per capita consumption of goods and services
- quantity of resources consumed, plus pollution generated during production and consumption through agriculture and industry.

As natural resources such as water, fuel and oil become scarce or less accessible, and it becomes increasingly difficult and expensive to provide them, the techniques of obtaining them are more likely to be environmentally destructive and more expensive. For example, fishing takes place in much deeper waters, or mining processes dig ever deeper into the earth searching for minerals such as coal or copper.

What is biodiversity?

Biological diversity – or biodiversity – means the number and type of species in an ecosystem, such as a tropical rainforest, a coral reef or wetlands, where many thousands of species interact in a complex system of linked, mutually advantageous relationships. Such ecosystems are valuable and hold barely tapped sources of foods and medicines, and encourage research in biotechnology (application of technological facts and principles to biological sciences), with important ecological functions. By destroying such ecosystems many plant and animal species are threatened by extinction. Once gone – they can never be replaced.

Profit and greed have damaged the environment

In both developed and developing countries efforts to generate financial gain as fast as possible have damaged natural systems, with little thought for future generations.

Sometimes, even when overused, some natural resources can restore themselves to a certain degree. For example, after overgrazing, grasslands may take a year to grow back. But after only moderate overfishing, five years may be needed for fish stocks to recover. Forest ecosystems may need 20 to 100 years to be replenished. Aquifers (layer of rock or soil able to hold or transmit water) can take between one and 1000 years to refill.

Generally, future development and rising in living standards will depend on how the natural environment continues to survive. The search is on for *sustainable development*.

> Do we still have a last chance...
> To make people realize,
> To give the children of tomorrow
> A chance to know
> The flight of the butterfly
> The song of birds
> (Adapted from 'A Poem from Sri Lanka', *Footsteps* 20.)

7.3 SUSTAINABLE DEVELOPMENT – WHAT DOES IT MEAN?

Sustainable development means meeting people's present needs while preserving nature's productive capacity for the future. It was a major focus of the United Nations Conference on Environment and Development, popularly known as the Earth Summit in June 1992 in Rio Janeiro, Brazil. The summit produced treaties to control global warming and to preserve bio-diversity. The Rio Declaration set out broad principles for environmental protection and sustainable development, and Agenda 21 was a detailed plan for combatting various environmental problems.

The earth's whole environment is made up of many linked factors, all of which play a part in maintaining its balance and wellbeing. In a sense, these factors maintain the health of the planet. For example, forests absorb both naturally produced and man-made carbon dioxide and lock it into their cycle of growth, giving off in the process the oxygen humans need to breathe. Plants and animals help maintain the environment and form the basis for the cultivation and production of food and essential products.

The next sections focus on why it is essential to preserve the earth's natural resources such as air, land, forests, wildlife, fresh-water resources, oceans and fishes, on which the livelihood and wellbeing of not only the poor and vulnerable – but all people depend. The sections have drawn par-ticularly on information from *Population Bulletin* (1992) and *Population Reports* (1992).

7.4 AIR, ATMOSPHERE AND OZONE

The earth is surrounded by a protective atmospheric layer which provides one of the essential ingredients for living things. The density of various del-icately balanced gases in the atmosphere determines the amount of sun's heat that reaches the earth, the amount trapped in the atmospheric layer and the amount that escapes back to space. The protective layer acts like a greenhouse in that it holds back some of the heat reflected by the earth. In this way, regulation takes place of the earth's natural climatic conditions. The correct amount of warmth and moisture is created for life to survive on earth. But *global warming* is damaging this natural process. It is caused by the massive quantities of gaseous emissions, such as burning of coal and gas, generated by human beings, particularly during industrial processes over the last decades. As these newer gases build up, the atmosphere ends up trapping more heat than before. It is this that is leading to global warming and to the rise in average global temperature. One result of global warming could be a rise in the level of the oceans by up to a metre, flooding coasts and displacing millions of people. Another result could be changes in rainfall, wind pattern and soil moisture.

The ozone layer and health effects

Ozone – a pungent, slightly bluish gas – collects 10–50 kilometres above the earth's surface. This ozone layer protects the earth from certain types of ultraviolet light emitted by the sun. One type of ultraviolet light can damage genetic material, reduce the human body's ability to combat cancer and suppress the immune system, increasing vulnerability to infectious diseases. This type of ultraviolet light can also penetrate deep into clear water, harming small sea creatures as well as plants essential to the marine food chain. Crops may also be sensitive to it. The ozone layer has been depleted (to create a hole in the ozone layer) by use of chlorofluorocarbons (CFCs), which are chemicals used in aerosols, refrigerators, air condition-ers, foams and solvents. CFCs can remain active for as long as a century.

7.5 SOIL DEGRADATION AND AGRICULTURAL PRACTICES

What causes soil degradation? Causes include water or wind erosion, loss of chemical nutrients, concentration of salts or acidic chemicals, compaction (where soil loses its structure, so that plants cannot develop healthy root systems and the soil cannot retain moisture and nutrients) and waterlogging. Other causes are overgrazing (responsible for 35 per cent of all degraded lands), faulty agricultural practices, cutting of forests for farming and logging, and stripping land for fuelwood. Shifting cultivation systems are often mentioned as prime causes of environmental degradation, but according to some, such systems have the potential to become settled systems supporting higher population densities through soil conservation, fertility-enhancing practices and possibly irrigation. However, where very rapid population growth occurs, technologies appropriate to lower densities tend to persist – and there is little time for learning/making a transition. This is how environmental damage is caused.

Drylands and desertification

Over a third of the earth's land area is classified as dryland, with low and erratic rainfall and a hot sun. What rain does fall soon evaporates in the heat. Globally, 39 per cent of the earth is classified as humid, 13.5 per cent as cold, 12 per cent as arid, 18 per cent as semi-arid and 10 per cent as dry sub-humid (United Nations Environmental Programme). Shallow dryland soil looks dry and dusty, perhaps with rocks showing through. Main causes of desertification are: loss of soil and soil erosion, inadequate fertilisation, overfarming land without giving it a chance to recover, lack of soil moisture, fragile soils, scarce vegetation, low rainfall and steep slopes. Indirect causes include: poverty, land shortage, use of unsuitable farming technology, land tenure patterns (where farmers do not own the land they farm and are reluctant to invest time and money to improve it), government policy and global climatic changes (ODA 1995).

Around a quarter of the world's population live in dryland areas and as many as 900 million people may be affected by desertification. Some live right on the borders of deserts, where drought is a constant threat. Many others in dryland areas have to cope with *desertification*, which refers to fragile dryland soils damaged by human activity and climate changes. There are also hyper-arid drylands, which are deserts where very few people live.

Because of soil degradation, large portions of the semi-desert areas of Africa are no longer able to feed their populations. For example, the whole Sahel region (north western African countries) could, it is said, reach this point within a decade.

Many problems attributed to drought, such as dry lands and reduced crops, are really symptoms of overuse of the land. For example, wells dry out when repeatedly drained and soils lose moisture when vegetation is cut. A crust forms on land that has been farmed extensively without appropriate conservation measures. Overcultivation and overgrazing leave marginal lands less able to retain water and more prone to erosion and the formation of salt deposits. Each year, worldwide, one billion tons of topsoil are lost as a result.

Some agricultural practices have damaged the environment

Agriculture both affects and is affected by the environment. Some forms of agricultural have not caused degradation of the environment, but many more recent ones have, such as massive clearance of rainforest in the Americas. Heavy use of fertilisers and pesticides can also damage the environment. Most destructive agricultural practices are driven by two factors, poverty and rapid population increase.

Over-rapid population growth plays a part in forcing farmers to cultivate areas that are dry, hilly or rocky, or which have thin, weak soils. Areas which could once support small numbers of people, or which were used for grazing livestock, become degraded and eventually can produce little or nothing. As populations grow, some farmers are pushed onto semi-arid rangelands which previously supported only nomadic tribes, providing supplementary fodder and water for their livestock during droughts. Since these lands are now under cultivation, the livestock which once depended on them may suffer large losses during dry periods. Landscapes become strewn with the carcasses of cattle which died of starvation and thirst.

7.6 CAN FOOD PRODUCTION KEEP UP WITH POPULATION GROWTH?

The Food and Agriculture Organization (FAO) of the United Nations predicts that more than half of developing countries (62 of 115 studied) may not be able to feed their projected populations from their own lands by the year 2000, using current levels of farming technology. Most of the 62 countries may be able to feed about half their population from their own lands. Some countries can afford to import food, but this is more expensive than local production. It also uses foreign exchange, which could be used for other development purposes, like developing industry. More advanced farming techniques will be needed in future to cope with projected population increases, but there will be difficulties. For example, the average amount of crop land worldwide per person is projected to decline from 0.28 hectares per person in 1990 – to 0.17 by the year 2025.

Three factors will mainly determine whether food production can be increased fast enough to keep up with population growth: whether new land can be put into production to offset the amount which becomes degraded through erosion, dryness, salt deposits or water saturation; whether agricultural need for water can be met; and whether use of fertilisers and pesticides is sustainable.

7.7 THE VANISHING FORESTS

At current rates of forest clearing, most tropical forests will be severely damaged or destroyed within the next 20 years. Main causes of deforestation are: permanent conversion of forest to agricultural land (often driven by population pressures), inequitable patterns of land ownership, impact of the logging industry and demand for fuel wood. Asia is losing its forests the fastest, at a rate of 1.2 per cent annually, while Latin America is losing 0.9 per cent annually, and Africa 0.8 per cent. In the Philippines, only eight per cent of the forests that stood 50 years ago still stand today (Myers 1994).

Of the 76 countries that now have tropical forests, only four – Brazil, Guyana, Papua New Guinea and Zaire – may have large stands of undamaged forest remaining by the year 2010. To slow such depletion, many countries have started tree-planting programmes in Africa, Latin America and Asia. However, reafforestation replaces trees but not whole tropical forest ecosystems which have evolved over hundreds of thousands of years.

The endless search for fuel wood for cooking and heating

Half to two-thirds of the world's population still depend on fuel wood for heating and cooking, particularly in Africa where nine out of ten households rely on fuel wood for cooking. Already, city dwellers' demand for wood and charcoal has left many cities surrounded by rings of deforested land stretching as far as 100 kilometres. Rural women must spend more and more time, and travel farther and farther – even up to ten kilometres from their homes – in search of fuel wood. It is estimated that by the end of the century, three out of five people in developing countries may be without adequate fuel wood, or else forced to overcut forests in order to meet their energy needs. The search is on to find alternative sources of fuel for cooking, such as by tree planting and use of solar energy.

Uncontrolled logging also hastens deforestation

It is estimated that less than five per cent of unprocessed wood produced in developing countries is legally exported. Often, local politicians may be involved in the lucrative business of logging and, despite international attempts to reduce logging, it continues. Each year the precious and dwindling supplies of hardwoods, like mahogany, are torn out of the forests. Sometimes they are used in other countries to make coffins for the rich – which are then cremated. Vast tracts of forest have been cleared for cultivation in such a way that, when the thin layer of cultivable earth is worn out, the area turns into a wasteland in which nothing grows. (Cartoon reproduced with permission from South–South Solidarity, Bangalore, India.)

Why forests are important

The rainforests are essential to regulating the world's climate by cleansing the atmosphere and providing a source of moisture for rainfall. Forests also serve many other essential ecological functions. They retain soil (the topsoil of the planet is thin) and absorb water which helps to prevent floods, landslides and erosion. Deforestation can lead to increase in some human diseases. For example, sun-loving mosquito species will thrive when forests are destroyed.

Fuel, food and fibre harvested from forests for subsistence or sale are important to many rural communities, and particularly to poor people. For most rural people foods derived from forests, or from trees they maintain in their farming system, add variety to diets, improve palatability and provide essential vitamins, protein and calories. Forests and 'farmtree foods' are extensively used to help meet dietary shortfalls during particular seasons of the year, helping bridge hunger periods when stored food supplies are dwindling and the next harvest is not yet available. The last main role of forest foods is in emergency periods such as floods, droughts, famines and wars. Few foods can be digested uncooked, and cooking is necessary to remove parasites. Wood is still often a major source of cooking fuel in rural areas of many countries (Arnold & Kanowski 1993).

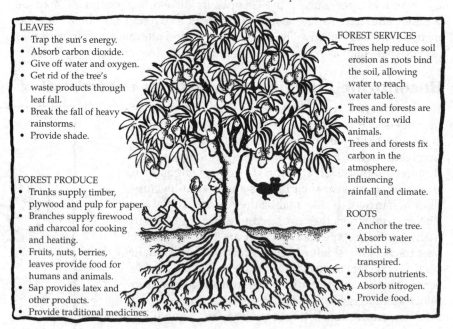

What Do Trees Do – Why Are They Important?

LEAVES
- Trap the sun's energy.
- Absorb carbon dioxide.
- Give off water and oxygen.
- Get rid of the tree's waste products through leaf fall.
- Break the fall of heavy rainstorms.
- Provide shade.

FOREST PRODUCE
- Trunks supply timber, plywood and pulp for paper.
- Branches supply firewood and charcoal for cooking and heating.
- Fruits, nuts, berries, leaves provide food for humans and animals.
- Sap provides latex and other products.
- Provide traditional medicines.

FOREST SERVICES
- Trees help reduce soil erosion as roots bind the soil, allowing water to reach water table.
- Trees and forests are habitat for wild animals.
- Trees and forests fix carbon in the atmosphere, influencing rainfall and climate.

ROOTS
- Anchor the tree.
- Absorb water which is transpired.
- Absorb nutrients.
- Absorb nitrogen.
- Provide food.

(Adapted from ODA (1992a).)

Fighting for the forests

The following example illustrates how, in the eighties and nineties, many NGOs have been involved in efforts to preserve or recuperate forest and farm tree resources.

7.8 WILDLIFE AND ITS HABITAT

Less than 200 years ago, biodiversity (the total number of ecosystems, species and genes on earth) may have reached an all-time high. At that time, there were one billion people on the planet. Today, the human population is over five billion, and increasing rapidly. At the same time, species of animals and plants are disappearing at an estimated rate of 4000 to 6000 a year and losses of this magnitude last occurred when the dinosaurs disappeared 65 million years ago.

While most losses of species occur in tropical rain forests, some also take place in dry forests, grasslands, temperate zones, wetlands and coastal habitats. Practices such as overharvesting, overfishing, indiscriminate use of pesticides, draining wetlands, polluting the air and water, and increasing urbanisation all contribute to diminishing the number of plant and animal species on the planet. So, as the number of humans increase, the number of plant and animals are decreasing.

Links between wildlife, natural habitats and human health

One reason why obscure plants and animals must be preserved is that future generations may be deprived of something valuable. Since we do not fully understand all the ways in which ecosystems work, by destroying a plant or animal species, an unforeseen chain of negative ecological events could follow. The important and often life-saving human medicine, penicillin, originated from a mould found growing on an orange. Wild species of plants have been used to make solutions which acted as natural pest control agents and some of the hormones used in oral contraceptives were extracted from roots that grow wild in Central America and elsewhere. A new drug being used to treat ovarian and breast cancer is made from the bark of a Pacific yew tree found in the United States, while a wild flower in Viet Nam and China has been found effective in treating the type of malaria which affects the human brain – and is often fatal.

Some of these treatments were found by accident, others through long-term research. As known and unknown plants disappear in deforestation and desertification, they take with them the potential of discovering new cures for old diseases – and perhaps for diseases which do not yet exist.

7.9 FRESH WATER – A DIMINISHING SUPPLY

Water covers more than two-thirds of the planet, largely in the form of oceans, seas, lakes and ice. The majority of this water is salty and cannot be used for human consumption or for irrigating plants. While countries can plan to make the best possible use of the water that exists in, or passes through the country, they cannot influence the rate at which water is naturally renewed through the water cycle (solar-driven circulation of water from the ocean, to the atmosphere, from the atmosphere to the land and back to the ocean). In other words, they cannot actually create more water.

Less than one per cent of the earth's water is unsalty and available for human consumption. In theory, this amount could support four times the present human population, but in reality water supplies are spread unevenly around the world. About two billion people in 80 countries live in areas of chronic water shortage – a situation that will worsen as human and animal populations grow. Particularly affected are most of Africa, the Middle East, north Asia and Australia. Many countries are draining water from aquifers (an underground level of earth or porous rock which contains water) faster than those aquifers can replenish themselves.

Due to population growth alone, water demand is expected to double in more than half of the world's countries by the year 2000. Most of this increasing demand is for irrigation and industrial uses. About 69 per cent of the world's fresh water goes for irrigation, about 23 per cent for industry and 8 per cent for household use. In many arid and semi-arid areas, population growth has raised food demand to a level that can be met only through irrigation. Some countries lie within climatic zones most prone to drought and other water problems. Unfortunately, some of these countries have high rates of population growth. For example, the populations of Kenya, Ethiopia and Iran may well double within 25 years, yet the amount of water available to these countries will remain the same (Falkenmark & Widstrand 1992).

Even with efficient irrigation and other water-use methods, many countries in the Middle East and Africa may not be able to meet their water needs by 2025 if population growth continues at present levels. By that date, some believe that as many as 25 developing countries may have reached the water barrier, which is the minimum amount of water needed by each person, assuming access to advanced technology to maximise water conservation. Another 24 countries may experience seasonal shortages and problems with water quality.

Access to water is not easy for the poor

In developing countries, people who are poor often use ingenious ways to get water. For example, in Manila, Philippines, poor families may make their own connections illegally, to tap into roadside municipal water supply pipes. Sometimes so many home-made connections are attached to the official pipes that there is little water left for the official receivers at the end of the line! In some urban areas the poor are forced to purchase drinking water and the cost may be high. For many of the urban poor, their environmental menu of choice is restricted, and they are more likely to get polluted air, contaminated food and dirty water.

7.10 DECLINE IN WATER QUALITY AND IMPLICATIONS FOR HEALTH

In many places water is declining in quality, resulting from some natural causes, but mainly from human activities and poor development strategies, such as those linked to mining, industrial production, timber and forestry, and certain farming practices (Platt 1995). Recorded outbreaks of shellfish poisoning have increased with pollution of water, in both tropical and non-tropical areas. One cause of shellfish poisoning is *red tides*, which are surface-to-deep water algal blooms (algae are simple organisms living in water and rocks) that float in a brownish-red or dark green mass. Red tides occur where there is a high concentration of nutrients and poor water drainage. The recent explosion in red tides is linked to growing aquaculture production (raising of plants, fish, shellfish in or under the sea, in a lake, river or other body of water).

7.11 HOW DOES FRESH WATER GET POLLUTED?

The main pollutants of fresh water are untreated sewage, and industrial and agricultural waste materials which pollute rivers, lakes and aquifers. For example, pesticides sprayed on crops can be washed off by rain to pollute nearby lakes and rivers. In Nicaragua, Central America, of the one million people who live in the capital city, 70 per cent use toilets that send waste to the nearby lake. The lake is now like an immense latrine and almost all fisheries, birds and plants have either died, migrated elsewhere or suffered illnesses from overdose of toxic waste (Platt 1995). In some Chinese lakes, 70 per cent of water consists of household sewage and industrial effluent, and in Cambodia the Great Lake is threatened by siltation from logging and deforestation.

The problem of disposing human excreta and domestic wastes

As a population grows, so does the volume of human excreta. Every year, each person produces fecal wastes which contain an average of 3.2 kg of nitrogen and 0.6 kg of phosphorus. More than 95 per cent of urban sewage in developing countries is discharged untreated into the nearest waterway, or on land such as a nearby field. In many slum areas, defecation and urination take place wherever there is a small open space/sheltered corner, and the excrement flows in narrow streams of contaminated water directly between the shacks/dwellings. Into these open sewers are also poured dirty household water, garbage and other pollutants. These streams disgorge into rivers or lakes from which the poor may draw their drinking water. This contaminated drinking water is a major source of disease among the poor, particularly among young children. Ironically, in urban areas, the more affluent use flush toilet systems which daily pour fresh water into sewage systems. Improved systems to deal safely with human excreta are urgently needed, especially those which use minimal fresh water, or preferably, use no water at all.

Industrial and agricultural pollutants and wastage

Industries waste large amounts of water and add toxic pollutants to water which could otherwise be reused. Factories and mines release large quantities of heavy metals, toxic chemicals and solid wastes into the water. For example, Lagune Lake in the Philippines has become heavily polluted by Manila's sewage, chemical wastes from around 900 factories, and fertiliser and pesticide runoff. A new water-control system intended to divert some of the pollution has further upset the ecological balance, reducing fish catches even more. When water dries up, it is lost forever. Some irrigation methods are highly wasteful of fresh water, such as sprinkler systems. Around 70 per cent of water currently used in irrigation is wasted because it never reaches the crops and is not returned to the rivers for reuse. Some innovative irrigation systems use lines/hoses which have periodic outlets through which the water can reach the crops with minimum water wastage.

Taking action to reduce water pollution

Some developing countries, like Ghana, Indonesia and Mexico, have increased efforts to conserve fresh water supplies and prevent pollution, through water treatment plants, waste control, recycling and conservation. India has a project to clean up the River Ganges, the 1500-mile-long river which provides water to a third of the population. The Ganges carries the untreated sewage of 114 cities of more than 50 000 inhabitants each, as well as a wide variety of industrial wastes.

In some cases, however, remedial action is difficult.

From Experience

In Kenya, Lake Victoria, the world's largest tropical lake, has been described as a 'sick giant', damaged through population increase, clearance of lakeside vegetation (to plant cash crops), the booming fish export industry, disappearance of several native fish species and prolific dumping of untreated industrial waste. It took around 14 000 years for about 400 species of native lake fish to develop, but introduced fish species have resulted in reduction of native species to around 200.

Kenya's strict pollution laws are said to be rarely enforced because lakeside industries have ties with foreign investors. It is cheaper for polluting industries to pay occasional 10 000 shilling fines than to install equipment to treat effluent at a cost of US$2 million (Chege 1995). In 1994, the lake was also polluted by thousands of floating human bodies, a legacy of the carnage in Rwanda. (On p. 132, an encouraging example is given of a Kenyan initiative to save one of its other lakes).

In the next example, the possibility of effective action is doubtful.

From Experience

'At the beginning you drink water – at the end you drink poison.' (Uzbek proverb.)

Once the world's fourth largest lake, the Aral Sea, bordering Uzbekistan and Kazakhstan in Central Asia, has been reduced to three separate highly saline lakes. Virtually no fish are now harvested from the once fish-rich sea, deeply affecting the livelihood of local fishing communities. The former seabed is exposed and dust storms scatter salt and pesticide residues over the whole region. The sea used to buffer cold Siberian winds and act as an air conditioner in the summer. With contaminated water and soil, human cancers have increased, with an estimated 70 per cent of the people in one nearby town having pre-cancerous conditions. (There was also atomic and hydrogen bomb testing previously in the area.) Eighty per cent of all women in the region suffer from anaemia, and nearly all haemorrhage while giving birth. Of every 100 newborn babies, 21 have birth defects. The former seabed is now a saltpan desert, a virtual graveyard littered with the rusting remains of fishing trawlers and bleached bones of cattle which died from eating salt-poisoned vegetation (Hinrichsen 1995).

Fortunately there are some examples of effective action against pollution of fresh water.

The pink flamingos that feed along the shore lines of Kenya's Lake Nakuru attract more than 100 000 tourists every year, but due to high population increase, surrounding forests have been cleared for farming. During the rainy season topsoil is washed down into the lake and the nearby town discharges large amounts of domestic and urban waste into the lake, including from a tannery and agrochemical and battery factories. Local groups are trying to reverse this environmental destruction. An education centre has been set up, along with courses on environmental education. Local community leaders (chiefs, teachers, government officials) and school children learn how their activities affect the environment; they see how the park and lake raise money, including for local communities. Workshops are run for women's groups on growing and planting trees, agroforestry, soil conservation, and making compost. The struggle for this environment continues.

It is not easy sometimes for the poor and hungry to understand and accept environmental arguments why they should not catch too many fish, or catch fish in the breeding season.

7.12 THE OCEANS AND THEIR FISH

In addition to providing food, oceans help to regulate climate and protect against extreme temperature fluctuations. Oceans also absorb 30–40 per cent of the carbon dioxide emitted by human activities. Even minor changes in ocean temperature, chemistry or circulation patterns could alter the ocean's absorption of carbon dioxide; a change that could hasten the warming of the global climate. Depletion of the ozone layer in the upper atmosphere could reduce the growth of plankton, which are microorganisms that form the basis of the food chain for fish.

About 60 per cent of the world's population live within 100 km of ocean coasts. Thirty of the world's largest cities are located on or near the coasts. Coastal population densities reach more than 500 people per square kilometre in several Asian countries, more than twice the density inland. As these urban populations increase, efforts to produce food for them contributes to overfishing. Nearly a quarter of the world's animal protein supply comes from fish. Overfishing, habitat destruction and pollution cause decline in fisheries, and globally, more than one in five freshwater fishes may be threatened or endangered (Platt 1995). Demand for fish continues to grow.

But growing human settlements are destroying the coastal areas that serve as hatcheries for 90 per cent of the world's fish. For example, in Jakarta, Indonesia, many families used to make their living from fishing. The city's population doubled between 1970–90 and coastal waters became filled with untreated sewage and industrial wastes. Fish catches have been drastically reduced and the few which remain are unsafe to eat. Natural coastal ecosystems are being damaged by heavy pollution and by dredging and filling of wetlands to make room for further development. An analysis of 31 developing countries found that more than half of their mangroves (coastal forests) have been destroyed since pre-agricultural times.

Why are oceans treated as garbage dumps?

What is dumped into the oceans? Wastes from coastal cities, sewage discharged into upland rivers, sediment from tree cutting, and fertiliser and pesticide runoff all eventually reach the oceans. Sewage and sedimentation are now more serious sources of oceanic pollution than oil spills or dumping of toxic wastes. In many coastal areas, sewage and industrial waste have killed fish and contaminated shellfish beds. (Much oceanic pollution is also caused by western industrialised countries.)

Degradation of the oceans – implications for the poor

In many countries, sizeable proportions of coastal families who are poor rely on fishing for their livelihood, so when fish stocks are depleted or diseased, the base of their survival is undermined. Fish and shellfish, until recent decades, had been a reliable source both of food and of income, but in some places in Asia red tides of algae have decimated the trade in these products.

In many parts of the world dried or smoked fish are to be found far inland, providing an important source of nutrients for poor and vulnerable population groups. For those without access to refrigeration, dried or smoked fish is important.

Poor families who relied on reefs and reef products for their economic survival are also facing increasing problems. In many places reefs have been polluted by industrial wastes and oil discharged into the sea. The reefs were the centre of much marine life, but now they are lifeless. In some places in the Philippines, old tyres have been lowered offshore to create artificial reefs which can eventually attract back the marine life.

7.13 MINERALS AND METALS

The earth contains minerals and metals such as copper and zinc, which are dug, or mined from beneath its surface. There are precious metals such as gold, which are mined or dredged from rivers. Natural minerals and metals are non-renewable. Substitutes for some minerals and metals have been made, but never for gold. Due to rapid industrialisation, economic growth and population increase, the consumption of non-renewable and non-fuel minerals, metals and various other materials used in industry and construction has increased faster than the population. Since the 1970s, demand for metals has levelled off in developed countries and increased in developing countries. Whether future supply can meet demand is not clear because rates of economic growth are not known, and nor is the way in which minerals may be used more efficiently, recycled or even substituted.

Will the minerals and metals ever run out? Some predict that all known and predicted supplies of copper will last 277 years at current consumption rates, assuming no population growth. Minerals and metals will be increasingly difficult to extract from the earth. The scarcer a resource becomes, the more impractical and environmentally damaging it becomes to obtain it. It is necessary to drill deeper into the ground, spending more and using more energy to extract the minerals and metals.

A minority of people who are poor make livings – some even become wealthy – from activities such as gold prospecting (digging or dredging for gold), but for the vast majority of the poor, activities relating to minerals and metals benefit them little, if at all.

7.14 ENERGY SUPPLIES – OIL, COAL AND GAS

How long will non-renewable resources last? At current consumption levels, and assuming no population increase, some predict that readily accessible oil supplies could be exhausted within 40 years, and natural gas in 60 years. Coal supplies could last much longer – for hundreds of years, perhaps. However, switching to coal for energy supplies is said to be likely to worsen air pollution and hasten the onset of global warming. In developing countries the search for more sustainable use of energy is slowly advancing, but other factors and needs often receive priority. It is also expensive to develop alternatives.

7.15 HOW THE POOR SUFFER FROM ENVIRONMENTAL DAMAGE AND ACTION THAT CAN BE TAKEN

Most people who are poor live in areas that are described as *environmentally vulnerable*, which means that even minor changes in climate or land use can affect the quality of the local environment and its ability to support the local population. Such environmental damage therefore has a particularly severe effect on poor people. Even if environmental problems are short lived, they have no resources to tide them over until the crisis is past, nor do they have the resources to invest in measures and activities to confront new and long-term environmental changes.

There are environmentally damaging factors and consequences, like global warming, which can only be attended to through international action. Then there are those which depend more on national action, such as agricultural policies and control of mining activities. But there is some important action which people can take at district level to protect fresh water sources, renew forests and protect local wildlife. A practical step is for people to begin looking systematically at what is happening in their surrounding environment. The key questions in Appendix A may help in constructing an analytical framework of key questions appropriate to local circumstances. The questions help focus local natural resources, factors and practices harming them, and regulations/actions needed to prevent/ reduce further harm to the natural environment. They also consider who will take the action. The questions can be adapted for use during: a) a 1–2 hour exercise at a meeting/intersectoral workshop/training course using small group sessions; or b) community level 1–2 hour intersectoral focus group discussions. Optimally, the community will generate and prioritise their own local environmental key questions.

The following example shows how community action can result in posi- tive gains for the environment – and at the same time for health.

From Experience

In Honduras, Central America, forest areas inhabited by the Tawahka people were threatened by encroaching logging companies, cattle ranchers and farmers. They were helped to visit other Indian groups who had already seen their forests destroyed. Next they met cattle ranchers and farmers in areas which were being cleared. They heard that some farmers could not find land anywhere else, but others were motivated by greed, wanting quick profit from felling trees or breeding cattle. The whole experience was recorded on video and shown later to other Tawahka community members who became convinced of the need to protect the forest. Then the leaders met with government representatives to find out about their own legal posi- tion and rights. They made simple maps of the area, first drawn on the ground then transferred to paper, showing the extent of deforestation and the remaining rainforest. The maps were later used by the government to help plan a forest reserve, and by the press (with a video) to generate public understanding and support.

A man-made environment of conflict and violence has many negative effects on the poor and vulnerable.

7.16 AN ENVIRONMENT OF CONFLICT AND VIOLENCE FOR THE POOR

In 1993 there were reported to be over 30 civil wars being fought in the world. Factors which continue to lead to conflict and violence include ethnic factors, racial tensions, social inequities, unemployment, poor edu- cation and aggressive and/or corrupt policing. Conflict and violence both breed poverty and are outcomes of poverty. This is true both for western industrialised nations and developing countries.

In Latin America, causes of violence include internecine wars, political conflicts, social problems, economic crises, drugs production and marketing. It is more difficult to obtain international comparisons for non-fatal crime, because definitions may differ between countries. However, common types of non-fatal violence are robbery, assault and rape. In many countries of the world a principal cause of both non-fatal and fatal violence has been associated with repressive military regimes.

Death rates from homicide vary from country to country. In a list of 41 countries, between 1981–6, the list was topped by the USA, Ecuador and the Bahamas, with levels of 8.3 per 100 000 of the population, or more (nearly 12 times the rate for the United Kingdom). In Cali, Colombia, there were 90 deaths from homicide per 100 000 of the population in 1992. One in ten deaths in Cali in the first half of 1993 were carried out by adolescent gangs and one third by young hired killers. Many hospitals functioned mainly as war units to attend to victims of violence (Golding 1995).

What conflict and violence do to health

No proper assessment has been made of what conflict and violence have done to health services and health personnel in the affected countries. The evidence, still fragmentary, includes destruction of health facilities, and torture and killing of health workers. They have been targets, illustrating their value as local assets. As a result of such conflict and violence, health care, especially first aid, maternal and child health services (particularly immunisation) and disease prevention and control activities (like those against malaria, tuberculosis and leprosy) have been disrupted or halted.

Violence may continue to affect efforts to reconstruct and rehabilitate health services. In all cases, the costs to the local population have been heavy. Deprived of health care and services, diseases have raged unchecked, infant and maternal mortality have risen, medical supplies have been disrupted and hijacked, emergency referrals never take place, and what could have been preventable disabilities leave a sad legacy for their victims – who are often from poor and vulnerable groups. The poor continue to suffer long from the legacy of conflict and violence. For example, farming families who are poor in some parts of Asia and Africa are plunged deeper into poverty by the unexploded land mines which still lie in wait on their lands.

Initiatives are under way in some countries to assist in rebuilding war-torn societies. For example in Eritrea, where large numbers of people are still dependent on food aid, the food security situation is being examined and plans made to improve food security and assist self-settled groups to integrate into society. In Mozambique, where large parts of the infrastructure and productive and social sectors were damaged by war, plans are under way for rebuilding/rehabilitating infrastructure (including for health) and methods of financing this (UNRISD 1996).

There are also other types of social decay from which the poor and vulnerable suffer disproportionately.

7.17 THE POOR AND SOCIAL DECAY

Attention is drawn to decay in the natural environment, yet the same notion of decay is seldom applied, except by religious leaders, to the social environment. In Appendix B, some social decay indicators are included, such as estimated numbers of injecting drug abusers, and children who live and sleep on the street. It is often difficult to get accurate information for indicators of social decay as some acivities are illegal, such as the use of habit-forming drugs and sexual relations with minors. There may well be reluctance to admit that certain activities take place at all. Even societies which publicly maintain human value and dignity may, in fact, rate low on the 'healthy society' scale.

Signs of progress towards stopping social decay

A few western industrialised countries now have legislation to prosecute citizens who are known to have had sexual relations with minors (often poor children) while abroad. Other signs might include existence of mechanisms to identify, contact, assist and counsel injecting drug abusers. Without any action to identify and confront social decay, patterns of poverty and deprivation will be passed on to the next generations.

7.18 ECO-REFUGEES, FLEEING FROM ENVIRONMENTAL DEGRADATION

Eco-refugees are people who can no longer gain a secure livelihood in their homelands because of drought, soil erosion, desertification and other environmental problems, aggravated by pressures of population and poverty. In their desperation they feel they have no alternative but to seek sanctuary elsewhere (Myers 1994). Sometimes they relocate within the same country, sometimes they move across the borders into another country. In 1994, there were said to be 43 million refugees of all types (economic, political, environmental) – or one person in 200, globally. In some sub-Saharan countries, as many as one in ten members of the population is a refugee. Each day, it was estimated that as many as 5000 people find themselves obliged to abandon their homelands for environmental reasons. By 1994, there were estimated to be at least ten million eco-refugees, but in reality there may be as many as 25 million, and their numbers are increasing as poverty and environmental degradation increase.

As the refugee problem has been growing, resources to tackle it have been shrinking, but if the problem is not dealt with in the short term, it will become worse and more costly in the long term. Host countries will be increasingly unable to accommodate the rapidly growing refugee populations. Refugees, in desperation, cross national borders. They will congregate in destitute sections of the mega cities and will be dependent on city services which are often already overloaded. Otherwise, they will pour into crowded refugee camps with inadequate subsistance conditions. In some places, refugees have become victims of social discord and hatred. Ironically, the 20 countries with the highest ratios of refugees have an annual per-capita income of only US$700. Poorer countries have little chance of supporting or resettling refugees without external help.

OF SAFETY NETS AND COPING STRATEGIES

The chapter begins by looking at a traditional safety net system – the family. It then focuses on what a district safety net for the poor and vulnerable needs to include to meet basic and health needs, and how the poor can be targeted. How have national austerity measures affected the poor, and what can reduce these negative effects? Examples of safety net devices are outlined, particularly relating to food and health, including food banks, ration cards, food subsidies, food supplements through health facilities, food-for-work, low-cost restaurants, and fair-price shops. Next, the focus is on factors undermining access of the poor to social welfare, and whether health services themselves are becoming poverty stricken. A basic index of deprivation is suggested for stress assessment and support for households coping with HIV and AIDS. Finally, the chapter considers how the poor can be helped to cope better in the face of natural hazards, such as typhoons, and in disaster situations.

8.1 WHY SOCIAL SAFETY NETS ARE NECESSARY

A social safety net at national level usually consists of a combination of policies, legislation, financial and material resources and services, all directed towards preventing poorer and more vulnerable groups falling into poverty or sinking into poverty more deeply. Some safety nets are ancient – such as the family.

Family as a safety net device

The family is often the major source of the basic necessities of life and health, particularly in developing countries. The word 'family' covers a range of family-type options, such as traditional extended families (where several generations live together in a single household arrangement or remain in functional contact, despite living in different places) and the nuclear family (parents or step parents living in a single household with their children). Other family types include same-gender couples, single parents living with their children (such as widows, divorced parent, unmarried parent), grandparents living with their grandchildren (AIDS orphans, perhaps) and teenage AIDS orphans caring for their younger siblings. The type of family involved determines the type of safety net functions possible. For example, an extended family may be able to provide a better safety net than a struggling single-parent family or teenagers caring for their siblings.

Well-functioning family systems can provide a safety net to their members through minimising risks in rearing of the young, providing material and emotional support or caring for older people. They can provide a variety of role models which prepare children for adulthood. But badly functioning traditional family forms, for example where there is domestic violence or child abuse, cannot do some of these things. Whether a family – extended or other type – functions successfully as a safety net for its members depends on their perception of responsibilities, on the personalities involved and their standard of living. Even very poor but well-functioning families provide affection and assistance, and increase survival possibilities for their members. However, for any form of family life and family safety net, there are some factors which are combining to unravel it.

Factors which unravel the family safety net

The degree of parental control and responsibility has changed in many places, with the young – particularly in urban areas – often having more freedom in selecting friends, education, work, and a spouse. Because of changes in moral standards and behaviour, many parents feel ill equipped to help children prepare for experiences they themselves have never had. Adults are increasingly having to seek employment away from their families, including as migrant workers. In some places, rising divorce rates undermine the stability of family life. Above all, poverty, deprivation of basic needs (such as adequate food, shelter), opportunities for productive employment and limited access to services like education, health and agricultural extension, are combining to undermine family life. For the poor, and vulnerable, access to a well-designed safety net of social welfare components can mean the difference between surviving or not surviving.

8.2 WHAT SHOULD A SOCIAL SAFETY NET INCLUDE?

What a social safety net should include depends on particular circumstances. Different types of net are appropriate to different countries. For example, where poverty is confined to particular pockets/groups/areas, and poor and vulnerable groups are readily identifiable and targetable, social welfare schemes may be realistic. On the other hand, in countries where poverty is widespread but acute crises arise periodically – such as natural hazards and disasters (drought, floods, typhoons) or man-made disasters (war, political coups) – a social safety net will need to contain items in response to the particular time and event. For example, feeding programmes during drought. These may be quickly activated, and also quickly terminated when the emergency need is over.

Some countries have social welfare schemes which have been in progress for some time. A *welfare state* is one whose government provides for the welfare of its citizens, especially through a system of social security, unemployment insurance, free (or accessible) medical treatment and other related programmes. A *government social insurance* scheme insures a person against unemployment or illness through government action, for example through accident insurance, workman compensation, sickness benefit, and old age and unemployment insurance. For poor countries, constructing and maintaining some type of welfare provision for the poor and vulnerable has proved to be difficult, particularly where local institutions are not well developed.

Safety nets in relation to health

Health status is a major factor influencing the capacity of a poor family to move away from poverty. Unless household members can work, produce food crops/goods, save income, invest their savings and build assets, they cannot progress – or even maintain their position. The single most important factor in maintaining health is often nutrition. Investments made to help poor households to build assets and cross the poverty line are themselves vulnerable to erosion if hunger is ignored, if infection continues to rise and ill health secures a grip on the household.

Hunger and infection feed on each other. Together they contribute to relatively high infant and maternal mortality levels in poor families. A safety net which is not based on providing some security against hunger and ill health, is a flawed net. A social safety net has been likened to a 'basket' of essential commodities, made available to poor households as an entitlement and at a price, on conditions that they can afford.

Examples of district action for basic household needs

What kinds of district safety nets are needed? The following list relates basic household needs to examples of action. The list is brief, and many more examples can be provided in a particular district/location.

Examples of action needed in the district to supply basic needs at household level

1 **Food**
   - Food security at household level (not just national level).
   - Increased, decentralised food production using technologies relevant to deprived areas, such as arid lands.
   - Local production of basic staples (coarse grains, rice, root crops).
   - Fair-price shops, food banks, midday meal programmes for children.

2 **Adequate clean water**
   - Construction of low-cost gravity-feed systems in hilly area, hand-drilled wells and rainwater catchment tanks in coastal areas.

- Provision of technical assistance, and credit and savings schemes.
- Training of local people in maintenance of water systems.
- Clean water storage tanks or containers.

3 Shelter
- Low-cost housing options to protect from extremes of heat, cold, rain, wind, rodents and disease-causing insects.
- Screening of doors and windows.
- Smokeless ovens.

4 Land/money
- Access to land for household food production (as well as cash crops), livestock grazing access.
- Creation of productive employment opportunities, food-for-work programmes (especially during slack season).
- Access to income generation, credit and savings.

5 Human health care
- Training of community-based health workers (village/neighbour-hood volunteers).
- Training of traditional birth attendants.
- Training of health staff and orientation of clinics/health centres/hospitals to primary health care.
- Revolving funds for medicines, instruments and equipment.
- Targeting spending on high mortality areas, such as those affected by malaria.
- Low-cost sanitation and safe garbage disposal schemes.
- Schemes for purchase of low-cost spectacles, artificial limbs, locally made wheelchairs.

6 Animal health care
- Training of animal health assistants.
- Decentralised lower-level facilities supplemented by outreach programmes.
- Schemes for low-cost veterinary drugs.

7 Security/human affection
- Training of police in legal rights of women.
- Prosecution of criminal acts and rape cases.
- Training of health staff to recognise child abuse.

8 Energy
- Electrification of villages.
- Urban credit scheme for purchasing wiring and light bulbs.
- Subsidised kerosene for poorest families/beneficiaries.

9 Environmental health
- Tree-planting by school children.
- Environmental education in school syllabus.
- Prohibition of waste dumping in fresh water.
- Control of toxic wastes, such as local industry/productive enterprises.

- Health-promoting school programmes.
- Sex/family life education in syllabus.
- Adult literacy materials on HIV/AIDS.
- Family planning approaches targeted at men.

Some common methods of targeting the poor

Targeting can be directed at vulnerable groups and/or disadvantaged areas. There are two common methods of targeting a) using indicators to identify who qualifies, and b) self-selection where applicants screen themselves through a decision whether to become involved or not. Decisions on which method to use are influenced by factors such as administrative cost, practical feasibility and political acceptability.

Using indicators for targeting

People/households may be selected if they fall below a certain income level, live in a certain geographic location (such as remote areas or poorest urban slums), or have specific demographic characteristics (such as a number of children under five years of age). Using indicators for targeting may be easier administratively, but contains danger of leakage of benefits to the non-poor.

Using self-selection for targeting

The poor decide themselves whether to participate. By designing programmes which will appeal less to the non-poor, such as low-cost shelter, low-cost and low-status foods, low-paying jobs and elementary sanitation, leakage to the better off can be reduced. Rural public works schemes can target participants at the same time as raising incomes. Self selection is also useful for food and nutrition programmes (Ravallion 1991).

Safety nets for coping with impact of austerity measures on the poor

Safety nets and targeting are dominant issues in most poor countries, particularly in response to structural adjustment and the resulting austerity measures – from which the poor are often the first to suffer. They are the ones who cannot afford user fees or unsubsidised fertiliser. In Ghana, a set of reforms was launched under an *economic recovery programme*. The economy grew and by 1985 had reached a growth rate of 5.4 per cent with reduction of inflation rate from 123 per cent in 1983 to around 26 per cent in 1986 (Commonwealth Secretariat 1991).

The reforms then went into a second stage. However, concern grew about the way the structural adjustment plans (SAPs) were affecting poverty and their effects on vulnerable groups, especially women, children and rural dwellers. Many workers laid off in the public sector could not find jobs in the private sector. Cuts had been made in social expenditure, user fees introduced, subsidies reduced or removed on production, and the government role had shrunk in service provision. In Sri Lanka, which had pursued some similar policies including encouraging free imports, results included blunting of the competitiveness of locally produced agricultural substitutes, reduction of state support for agriculture and diminished production of some crops, such as red lentils, soya and maize, previously grown on marginal lands by the poor. Subsidies were removed on fertiliser, undermining the capacity of poor farmers to raise their incomes. The poor, who spent more than 80 per cent of their income on food, paid a higher proportion of their disposable income in relation to those better off.

Subsequent SAPs have been accompanied by *amelioration packages*, to offset the negative effects of adjustment programmes on poor and vulnerable groups. For example in Ghana a special government programme was introduced to target rural households with low productivity, poor access to social services and income-increasing opportunities, and who suffered particularly from unemployment and hunger during the lean season. Also targeted were low income, unemployed and underemployed urban households without productive economic opportunities, who suffered from price increases on essential commodities and retrenched workers without skills for productive employment.

PAMSCAD projects included public works, food for work, hand-dug wells, low-cost sanitation, nutrition and shelter. A revolving fund was set up for bulk purchase of food for pupils (often poor and from distant locations) at boarding schools. However, by 1991 PAMSCAD was reported to have too many projects relative to level of donor support and government administrative capacity to implement them. The poor had been targeted only with moderate success and projects had not been integrated into the mainstream government public investment programme.

Guyana in South America has created a Social Impact Amelioration Programme (SIMAP). In Bolivia, South America, an Emergency Social Fund was set up in 1987 and, for remote areas, clinics, schools, social and employment generation programmes were set up. NGOs and community organisations were also involved.

8.3 REACHING THE POOR WITH APPROPRIATE FOOD SCHEMES

The subsidising of grains and rice has been used as a way of increasing access of the poor to basic commodities, stabilising food prices and transferring income to the poor. But such subsidies are currently considered to lower the price of food grains and agricultural inputs, to impose heavy financial burdens and distort the way resources are allocated in an economy. It is also hard to prevent leakage to the non-poor. One strategy is to subsidise only coarser grains of wheat and rice which are not popular with the non-poor. (Subsidies have also been suggested on tubewells and fertilisers.) Food subsidies in Asia are said to have raised nutritional levels and improved school attendance. In Asia, credit schemes to support self-employment schemes are also helping to wean the poor away from dependence on food subsidies.

The table which follows lists types of food schemes designed to benefit the poor and increase their access to food. Schemes vary in scale, design, organisational mechanisms, types of food and commodities. Some involve decentralised agriculture and food production, and a large network of fair-price shops backed by often massive systems of procurement, storage and transport, and focused on remote and deprived households. Some are wage-employment programmes with an in-built food component, and some are supplementary feeding schemes.

ENABLING THE POOR TO FULFIL THEIR BASIC FOOD NEEDS

Type of scheme	Examples of who should benefit
Food stamps/coupons	Households with a monthly income below a specific amount.
Food banks	Those who live in areas affected by natural/man-made hazards and disasters. Households with working adults.
Fair price shops	Families with children under five years. Pregnant and lactating women.
Food for work	Those without land or stable employment.
Low-cost restaurants	Low-income slum households. Unemployed adults and young people.
Small-scale agricultural extension	Households linked to women's groups which grow and use cereals, beans and vegetables.
Health facility supplements	Malnourished children. Pregnant and lactating women. Households affected by chronic illness, e.g. TB, HIV/AIDS.
Creches/day-care centres	Children up to five years of age. Working mothers.
School system	School-age children who go to school.

What type of food scheme is appropriate in a particular district will vary according to whether there is a national scheme to promote food security or whether one of the smaller initiatives may help the poor and vulnerable in that place to fulfil their basic food needs.

Food stamps/coupons

The food stamps/coupons system allows poor and vulnerable people to exchange special stamps/coupons on a regular basis for food. Following a food subsidy scheme introduced as early as 1942 in Sri Lanka, a food stamp scheme was introduced in 1979 for low-income households (those earning less than 700 rupees monthly). By 1992 it was reported that about half the population (7.9 million individuals in 1.9 million households) were entitled to food stamps (Commonwealth Secretariat 1993a). In addition, there was a subsidy of 250 rupees a month, and those without electricity received monthly kerosene stamps worth 28 rupees. In Asia, food stamp schemes have been complicated by liberal targeting and rising inflation, which devalued the food stamps and reduced purchasing power (South Asian Commission 1992). In Bangladesh a Vulnerable Groups Programme was directed at children and pregnant and lactating women, and in India there was a Women and Children in Rural Areas Programme, a Socio–economic Programme for Scheduled Castes and Tribes, and a Drought Prone Area Programme aimed at small farmers and the landless.

From Experience

In Zambia, a 'mealie meal' coupon system was introduced, first covering the urban population, then later targeting those with low income. However, a 1989 study indicated poorest urban families could be worse off with the coupon system as it stressed reducing expenditure rather than improving food security. The number of participating retail food outlets were also reduced, making it harder for the poor to claim their food entitlements, and non-urban people and those in the informal sector – often the poorest – were left out, reducing the value of the system.

Another scheme involved urban self-help projects and local NGOs. At least 95 per cent of participants were women. Special feeding took place in Mother Care Health clinics, schools, health centres and in hospitals, where in 1992, the number of infants dying was reduced from ten a day to less than one (Government of the Republic of Zambia 1992).

Food banks

The food bank system involves a country or programme stockpiling food at a particular place (or places) to prevent famine in case of reduction of food stocks, usually through natural hazards such as drought or flood. Bangladesh maintains a 'buffer' stock of a million tons, enough to meet emergency needs for a period of three months.

Fair-price shops

A fair-price shop is a special shop where food and other basic local consumer necessities are made available for purchase at prices affordable by the poor. Such shops may be linked to other local assets (such as a school or women's credit group) to enhance the overall effect of action against poverty. If fair-price shops are open to poor and non-poor alike, they can be expensive to maintain, but the less poor may prefer to avoid the inconvenience of queuing for what they see as only modest savings. India's large Public Distribution System (PDS) involves procurement and distribution of around 20 million tons of food grain as well as kerosene and sugar, through 350 000 fair-price shops. Since 1992 the scheme has been particularly aimed at the rural poor, particularly in remote tribal communities and drought-prone or mountainous areas.

Food for work

This system involves employment of individuals and groups who are poor in work such as construction of roads, dams or irrigation systems. Instead of being paid wages they are paid the equivalent in food. For example, an Indian rural wage employment programme has a food grain component built in of two kilograms of grain per man day per participant. The food was delivered to the participating poor through fair-price shops (as above). Employment-oriented programmes and food-for-work schemes are self targeting, as only the needy and genuinely poor tend to come forward.

Low-cost restaurants

These are community-established restaurants where the poor can obtain a nourishing and inexpensive meal.

From Experience

In Peru, South America, the poor are using ancient principles of solidarity and mutual care to combat hunger and poverty. In the capital city, in 1994, there were reported to be 8000 milk distribution committees, bringing together mothers who were poor to prepare and distribute nearly one million rations of milk every day to children and pregnant or lactating women. In the whole country, around 900 000 lunches and 230 000 other meals were being subsidised or distributed free of charge. Mothers' clubs, people's educational organisations and creches worked to improve nutrition, child growth and household hygiene, collect garbage, install latrines and get safe drinking water. Support was provided by NGOs and funding agencies. Government health services were coordinating their activities with the mobilised community groups (Lazo 1994).

Small-scale agricultural extension

Many types of small-scale activities fall under this category, but particularly relevant are those enabling the poor to produce food for consumption rather than sale. These include provision of seeds, tools and technical advice to women's groups, to enable them to grow pulses, beans and vegetables. In urban areas this can lessen dependency on imported foods (such as bread made from imported wheat) or fast foods that are low in nutritional value, high in artificial substances and likely to be unhygienically prepared. In some places there are urban 'backyard gardens' where, in limited space, urban slum dwellers have learned how to plant onions, tomatoes and other vegetables with which to strengthen their daily diet.

Health facility supplements

Supplementary foods are supplied at facilities like health centres, under-five clinics and nutrition rehabilitation units (usually simple structures adjoining hospitals or health centres, attended by mothers with malnourished children for 3–4 weeks). The child is rehabilitated (with frequent small high-quality meals) and the mother taught to make best use of local foods and improve household food garden production. The system works best where there is follow up and home visiting – or else the child may return in the same condition. The iron content of breast milk is inadequate after the child reaches six months of age. A decline in a child's weight increase, or actual loss of weight, are often early signs of malnutrition. Locally trained volunteer nutrition scouts (including school-age children), as used in Zimbabwe, can be trained to recognise the early stages of malnutrition, advise on infant feeding and refer serious cases.

Creches and day-care centres

These are organised child care facilities, usually run by trained staff, providing day care for babies and young children of working mothers in rural and urban areas. Some can provide meals for the children, where they are supported by the state/a local cooperative/private agency/parents who can afford to pay. But in creches and day-care centres in poor areas, and which have very little financial support, neither the babies or young children – or their carers or parents – may have enough to eat. There are neither funds to purchase food or donated foods with which to prepare an adequate daily meal. In some places innovative schemes have been set up, often through NGOs, to help poor women who work outside their homes to provide at least one adequate meal a day for their young children. For example, for women working on building sites, local volunteer women set up a mobile creche on the site. While mothers work, volunteers care for their children, cooking a basic meal for them at midday.

School system

There are various food schemes which can benefit children who attend school, including midday school meals, planting of school food gardens (tended by children, teachers, parents) and nutritional supplements for children found to be malnourished through simple nutrition screening approaches (like regular weighing by local health staff or involvement of children themselves in using a specially designed wall chart to assess normal height in relation to weight). However, such schemes are designed to benefit children who attend school. For school-age children who do not attend school (who might be too poor to afford registration fees or have to care for babies or livestock), their needs for adequate food during critical periods of growth are neglected. Some innovative education schemes to reach such children can include nutrition and health action. Generally, food schemes linked to school systems have to guard against pilfering and unjust food distribution.

To be really effective, food schemes to benefit the poor need to be integrated with activities, such as improved methods of household food production, processing, storing and preparation, improving access to fertile land, or space in urban areas (for backyard gardening to grow vegetables), and to generation of income through productive employment. In some places, people who are poor have been involved in local production of dried foods, cooking oil and macaroni. What is appropriate in a particular place will depend on causes and circumstances of poverty. For example, do those who are poor have to depend on scavenging rubbish dumps for edible scraps of food, or are they poor because drought decimated their harvest? Different participatory food schemes can be designed for both.

8.4 HOW ARE THE HEALTH SERVICES COPING?

Public health services are often struggling daily to survive themselves. Budgets have been cut and facilities are often deteriorating. There have been staff cuts, funds for maintenance have been reduced or cut, flows of medical supplies and equipment have dried up and some equipment is not functioning. Health staff have to cope with dilapidated accommodation and infrequent salaries, so that feeding their own families becomes a problem and their own basic needs such as shelter and food are threatened. Morale may be understandably low. Health facilities and staff from the non-government sector usually fare better, but lack of resources is also putting a strain on them too.

Health staff often struggle to provide basic health care under poor conditions and in remote locations. They, together with a range of co-workers (including auxiliaries, community health workers, traditional birth attendants) are like an army deployed on the primary health care front line. But they are increasingly an army without boots. With decentralisation, it should be easier for districts to know clearly the circumstances of their own health workers and co-workers, but targeted action to support their work seems to be lagging behind. One reason is that not enough opportunities are provided for them to articulate and prioritise their basic needs. These are usually more regular pay (to feed their families and pay school fees), attention to their living accommodation (repairs, safe water, sanitation, electricity/lighting, fuel), sufficient medicines and vaccines, standard treatment guidelines, and basic medical instruments and equipment for basic diagnostic and treatment purposes. Without the latter there can be no quality care.

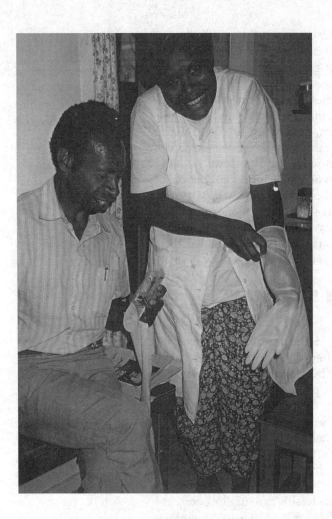

Where are the safety nets for health workers themselves?

Many professional health workers are poorly or infrequently paid. Many migrate from rural to urban areas – and even out of the country. It is often the best qualified nurses who migrate, leaving critically needed positions in educational institutions and government health care services vacant or filled by people who are less qualified (WHO 1996d). Despite frequent rhetoric over the past two decades, very little has been done about these kinds of problems. Countries are robbing themselves of a section of the professional workforce which is of particular significance to people who are poor and vulnerable.

Other factors are reducing this workforce in some countries. In Zambia, AIDS-related mortality among nurses rose from 2 per 1000 in 1980–5 to 26.7 per 1000 in 1988–90 (UNAIDS 1996). A whole range of approaches and safety net devices are therefore needed, such as special credit and savings schemes for nurses, midwives and middle-level professional health workers, and more effective targeting of support for health workers with chronic illnesses.

8.5 HIV AND AIDS IN RELATION TO POVERTY

People who are poor often come late for diagnosis, and thus late for treatment of early signs and symptoms. They are less likely to get treatment for sexually transmitted diseases (STDs), known to be a major factor aiding transmission of HIV, and less likely to get and use condoms. Poor migrants are particularly vulnerable to HIV infection, separated as they are from wife/partner and liable to turn to commercial sex workers. For women who are poor, sex becomes a commodity to sell, to obtain money, satisfy hunger of dependants, and clothe and educate children. Sex in poverty situations is sold very cheaply as there are many buyers and sellers.

The degree to which HIV infection and AIDS affects a poor household depends on its poverty level, and the stage of the infection. For example, after infection there may be a long stage without any symptoms, and normal occupations may be pursued. It is during bouts of illness that coping capacities are tested. Where most HIV transmission is sexual, both spouses may be ill at the same time, with the burden of care falling on the children or a relative. Many cases of HIV are detected in a couple when a newborn child fails to thrive or dies of an AIDS-related illness. Urban patients sometimes move back to rural areas to be looked after by relatives, and rural patients move to towns to take up trading when they can no longer farm. The loss of both parents means that surviving children will be orphans, and concern over their future is often the worst problem the couple has to face during illness. In Uganda, one study revealed that orphans are looked after by the following guardians: 17 per cent by their father, 26 per cent by their mother, 38 per cent by their grandparents, 7 per cent by aunts, 5 per cent by sister/brothers and 2 per cent by children under 16 years of age (Masaka 1993).

A household affected by AIDS often starts to become poorer by having to hire oxen (if they do no own them) for planting, which family members are too weak to do themselves. They may then have to hire expensive labour to do weeding. Apart from the main staple crop, other crops may drop out of production, reducing food availability to the household. Diets decrease substantially. It is considered that unless men assist women in labour tasks – which until recently were only performed by women – poverty, food insecurity and vulnerability will increase. In some areas of Zambia, for example, men have begun to acknowledge women's rights to have separate credit, fields and income, and are letting the women sell their own crops in the market.

After the death of a breadwinner from AIDS, the household sometimes splits apart. For example, in parts of central Africa, custom results in the dead husband's relatives arriving soon after or even before his death to claim all household possessions – right down to the last cooking pot. Although some laws have been passed to prevent this continuing, it remains a problem in both rural and urban areas. A widow may be left without the means to earn a living or to provide for essential family needs, forcing her to return with her children to live with her own relatives. In rural areas of Africa, families of AIDS patients will spend a lot of money for medical expenses and care, even up to 28 per cent of a total monthly wage.

In Uganda families reported selling property to pay for medical treatment and burial costs (UNAIDS 1996).

8.6 STRENGTHENING COPING STRATEGIES FOR POOR HOUSEHOLDS

In many places in Africa, the burden of caring for patients with HIV infection and AIDS is falling on families, as members take unpaid leave from work to act as carers. Children also take time off from school to care for family members who are sick. The burden of home care predictably falls on women. This means that women may have less time for agriculture. Since they are major food producers, this has repercussions on family diet and income. A study of relatives of AIDS patients admitted to a Zambian hospital found relatives willing to care for the patient, but barely equipped to do so. For example, diarrhoea was particularly difficult for poor households which had no running water or toilet. Home carers lacked food and money for medication.

Hospitals themselves are often inundated by AIDS patients. In main hospitals of some sub-Saharan cities (Kinshasa, Lusaka, Kigali, Bujumbura), 40–70 per cent of medical wards are occupied by patients with one or several HIV-related illnesses (UNAIDS 1996). Health staff absenteeism is also high, around 15 per cent in some places, and one third is attributable to HIV. Some health facilities have established outreach services to support home-based care of people with AIDS in the community. Communities have been mobilised, and networks formed that are linked to the nearest health facility. Home care is often preferred to hospital care because good basic care can be given successfully at home and people who are very sick – or dying – would often prefer to stay at home and will often recover from specific illnesses faster at home than in hospital.

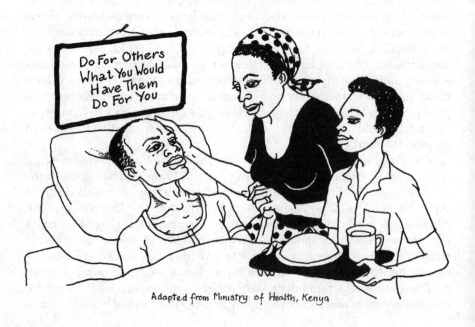

Adapted from Ministry of Health, Kenya

Some home-care programmes target people who are sick with other chronic illnesses besides AIDS. They include care for people with tuberculosis and malaria, and who are malnourished or weakened by old age. Some NGOs have developed to cater exclusively for the needs of individuals/families affected by AIDS. For example, CONCERN in Uganda has provided training and support to build on existing community safety nets supplied by the *Munno mukabi* informal village groups made up mostly of women, who traditionally support each other in times of need, such as by cooking at funerals and weddings. Representatives from such groups (and also from youth groups and football clubs) and village committee chairmen in 17 villages, were trained to care for and support people with AIDS. They care for anyone with a chronic illness in the villages. Each trained 'visitor' looks after about 20 households, building up trusting relationships through weekly visits (Brehony & Ssemulassa 1992).

For people with HIV and AIDS who have abandoned their families – or been rejected by them – the situation is often very bad. Such individuals in urban areas may not be receiving treatment. For example, in 1993, there were reported to be several dozen destitute patients living in the bus station of a major African city.

Assessing the coping capabilities for basic needs and care

In many families and communities basic needs such as food, clothing and housing are in short supply. An index illustrating level of deprivation and stress can help to reveal particular need and to target support to families least likely to cope. From the 60 variables listed below, perhaps 20 may be selected to form a useful index.

Each of the 20 variables is given a score of one. When the variables are applied to a low-income HIV/AID affected household, if that household scores over ten, it may be considered a high-risk household; one that is not coping due to a range of deprivations and stresses.

Towards an index of deprivation and stress assessment for low-income HIV/AIDS-affected households

1 **Family size and characteristics**
   - Number of people in household.
   - Age and gender of family head.
   - Number of school-age children.
   - Able to pay school fees for school-age children.
   - Number of dependants under five years of age.
   - Number of dependants over 65 years of age.

2 **Food security and preparation**
   - Household eats ... times a day (in relation to local custom).
   - Diet is below minimum national recommended calorific intake.
   - Experiences food shortages between harvests.
   - Owns livestock.
   - Eats own livestock products.
   - Availability of cooking fuel, e.g. firewood/kerosene/gas.

3 Water, sanitation and hygiene

- Safe drinking water available within dwelling, e.g. piped.
- Easy access to drinking water, e.g. communal standpipe, well.
- Sufficient water for patient care, e.g. wash body, bed clothes.
- Safe disposal of human excreta, e.g. pit latrine/toilet.
- Regular disposal of garbage, e.g. collection/burying/burning.
- Safe disposal of soiled dressings/cloths used by patient.
- Effective drainage for household waste water.
- Availability of soap.
- Dwelling is swept/cleaned once a day.
- Household owns additional buckets.

4 Shelter, security and protection from pollution

- Dwelling has roof which protects from rain.
- Room where patient is has a window.
- Doors and windows can be locked.
- Household members own warm clothes for winter.
- Household owns blankets.
- Household owns clean cloths for dressings.
- Dwelling is free of rodents and insects, e.g. rats, cockroaches.
- Air is not being polluted, e.g. by chemical emissions/dust.
- Patient has some privacy if required.

5 Land/production/employment

- Access to sufficient fertile land for home food production.
- Access to agricultural products, e.g. fertiliser.
- Availability of draught animals (if used).
- If owning livestock, access to grazing land.
- Time of women carers taken away from agricultural/food production.
- At least one adult household member in productive employment, e.g. sells produce/product, salaried.
- Access to markets for sale of produce/products.
- Has children in productive employment.
- Household is below upper poverty line (as defined nationally).
- Household is below lower poverty line (as defined nationally).
- Still owns saleable assets.
- Has been forced to sell assets.

6 Health care and support

- One household member has HIV infection or AIDS.
- More than one member has HIV infection or AIDS.
- Household member(s) with AIDS are bed ridden.
- Household member(s) with AIDS are experiencing severe symptoms, e.g. severe pain, severe diarrhoea, dementia.
- Availability of household member as full-time carer.
- Distance from health centre/hospital.
- Patient(s) receiving regular treatment for early diagnosed illnesses.

- Access to prescribed medicines, e.g. received free/exemption from fee/can pay.
- Patient(s) still fairly mobile.
- Patient(s) in terminal illness stage.
- Availability of volunteer workers to support carers.

7   **Psychosocial and spiritual needs**
- Protected sexual practices, e.g. access to and use of condoms.
- Freedom from stigma and discrimination.
- Regular visits by religious leader.
- Availability to patient(s) of recreational or creative activities.
- Supportive local community/neighborhood.

The next section of this chapter looks at how the poor and vulnerable can be helped to survive some of the most damaging effects of natural hazards and disasters.

8.7 NATURAL HAZARDS AND DISASTERS – HELPING THE POOR TO COPE BETTER

Natural events only become hazards and disasters when they threaten people or property. What makes a disaster? There are two main components, unsafe conditions and a natural event. The unsafe conditions may be the fragile physical environment, where the location is perhaps prone to flooding, typhoons or mudslides. The natural hazard is often blamed for the disaster, but the real cause may be the poverty of the people and the fact that they were unprotected. Many people who are poor know that they are living in areas of high risk to hazards and disaster, such as earthquake zones, flood plains, unstable steep slopes, and mudslides. They simply cannot afford to live anywhere else. They have no choice but to take those risks (Davis 1994).

Once a disaster has taken place, the first step is relief, including provision of food, water, clothing, shelter and medical care to the victims. Relief work usually lasts several weeks. With disasters and drought it may last months or even years. The second step is recovery and restoration, involving help to restore basic services which the people need so that they can try to rebuild the pattern of life which they had before the disaster. The third step is restoration, involving rebuilding of homes and businesses. Safety is important in the design of stronger buildings, able to withstand future disasters.

8.8 ACTION TO MINIMISE IMPACT OF DISASTERS ON THE POOR

Understanding the real causes of disasters helps people to realise how situations can be improved to help the poor protect themselves to some extent from hazards which can turn into disasters. For example, safer locations can be selected for buildings/shelter, and improved building methods and materials can strengthen them. Reforestation can reduce likelihood of soil erosion and flooding. A stronger local economy can reduce local poverty, making it a little easier for those who are poor to cope with disasters and to rebuild their lives. Risks can be reduced by putting in place early warning systems, such as typhoon/hurricane/earthquake surveillance, which can transmit warnings by telephone/radio/fax at least 24 hours in advance. Wind breaks can be built to protect housing, and dykes to prevent flooding. Well-designed irrigation systems can also reduce flooding risks. If such steps are taken, lives can be saved, casualties and injuries reduced and damage restricted. No measures can ever fully protect against all possibilities, but if put into place, they can greatly minimise the effects of disasters.

How can poor and vulnerable communities take steps to protect themselves from future disasters? How can they protect their dwellings, their property, their livestock and above all, their lives? The following table outlines practical action which poor households may be able to take for protection against disasters. The table has been adapted from Davis (1994).

PRACTICAL ACTION AGAINST DISASTERS AND FOR HEALTH

The natural hazard	Some practical measures
Tropical storms	Plant wind breaks of trees/bushes. Tie roofs down with ropes/heavy weights. Build strong buildings.
Floods	Water storage measures. Build overflow channels. Place sandbags at door of household. Build farm stores on high ground. Do not put electric sockets at ground level. Plan escape route through roof. Plant flood-tolerant crops, e.g. sorghum. Build walls/dykes/barriers to prevent flooding.
Mudslides	Build dwellings out of path of known mudslides.
Earthquake	Strengthen all new buildings – tie roofs, walls and foundations together with metal or timber bars. Build strong churches/community halls/schools, as people often gather there for protection.
Drought	Irrigation. Avoid or control soil erosion. Water-harvesting measures. Build grain stores to store surplus food during good years.

Basic first aid can prevent death and disability

Knowing what to do and how to cope if someone is injured can prevent unnecessary death or later disability. People who are poor often have their own first aid procedures, such as using a paste of local leaves to stop bleeding or making a rough splint for a broken leg. Many such practices are valuable, especially if strengthened by training in basic first aid. People who are poor and vulnerable can be rapidly cast into absolute poverty by a disaster which results in deaths and disabilities, but do opportunities exist in a particular district for people who are poor to learn first aid? Perhaps there is a local Red Cross or Red Crescent branch, or a health worker from a hospital or health centre who can help arrange first aid training for those who want to learn?

8.9 COPING WITH DISABILITIES – WHAT THE POOR CAN DO WITH SUPPORT

There are many causes of disability, for example as a result of natural hazards and disasters, birth injuries or occupational and traffic accidents. Poverty itself can increase the likelihood of becoming disabled. For example, poor people are more likely to live in unhealthy or dangerous environments. If they are employed, they are more likely to have jobs which are low paid, insecure or dangerous. Workshops and factories with bad lighting and a smoky atmosphere can cause visual impairment, and unguarded machinery is dangerous to limbs. It is estimated that more than 50 per cent of disabilities in developing countries could be prevented. People who are poor may be exposed to insecurity or violence in their homes or communities; they are more exposed to pollution and natural disasters. They are also more at risk of infection, and when they are ill they have less access to treatment. Disabled people are more likely to suffer general ill health and to die at a younger age than non-disabled people, and poverty widens the gap still further (Tiroler 1995). To be both poor and disabled is a double disadvantage. Even when resources exist to help people in this situation, they may not know of them or have access to them.

Action for community-based rehabilitation (CBR)

Community-based rehabilitation (CBR) can play a valuable role in helping to prevent disabled people and their families from falling further into poverty. It does this by providing locally based rehabilitation services, by supporting education for disabled people and through training and income-generating schemes. It helps disabled people and their families to participate more fully in community life, and builds on resources available in the local community. These resources are the disabled person, his/her family and neighbours. Because CBR is carried out at home or in the neighborhood, poor villagers, city dwellers, refugees and other disadvantaged groups can benefit. Local people are trained and educated to work in CBR, including some who work voluntarily (Tiroler 1995).

THE COSTS OF PRIMARY HEALTH CARE FOR THE POOR

The chapter begins by considering whether basic health care costs are currently being shifted to the poor. What does a poor household need to keep healthy and how much does it cost? How can an *essential minimum health care package* help, and how can it be delivered? How much does such a package cost – and who can pay for it? What do cost recovery and user fees mean to the poor? Are those who need exemption getting it? What are poor households actually spending on health – and disease? What types of health financing mechanisms are being used to support primary health care, such as revolving drug funds, health insurance and credit schemes? These questions are considered as they affect people who are poor and vulnerable, particularly at district level.

9.1 SHIFTING THE COSTS OF BASIC HEALTH CARE TO THE POOR

In many places the costs for basic health care are being systematically shifted from the public sector to the individual consumer. Currently health sector reforms emphasise improved government spending on health, and promotion of diversity and competition in provision of health services. They try to reduce public spending on some less cost-effective health interventions and increase it on essential and more effective programmes. There are attempts at equity. However, the benefits of such attempted reforms have been mixed.

Currently, a limited package of public health measures and essential clinical interventions are being recommended by UN agencies and other international organisations. Can this help the poor and vulnerable groups any better than past approaches? What does it mean in practice at district level, and what will it cost to implement?

9.2 COSTING AN ESSENTIAL MINIMAL HEALTH PACKAGE

The World Bank's 1993 *World Development Report* outlined a basic two-part package (public health and clinical services). The public health part consists of immunisation; micronutrient supplements; school health programmes to treat worms and micronutrient deficiencies and provide health education; programmes to increase public knowledge for family planning and nutrition, self care and indications for seeking additional care; programmes to reduce consumption of tobacco, alcohol and other drugs; and AIDS prevention programmes with a strong STD component. The cost of this package in the poorest countries could be US$12 per person per year. Yet in 1991, the government of Uganda spent only US$1.30 per person, and the government of Nepal only US$0.90 (Gilson 1994). For a poor country to be able to afford such a package would probably require a quadrupling of expenditure on public health.

As well as a public health package, a *minimal package of essential clinical services* was defined, acknowledging that, in practice, a patient's health needs often require several linked interventions. For example, a child with fever and diarrhoea may require treatment for both acute respiratory and gastrointestinal infections. The package consisted principally of antenatal and delivery care, family planning services, management of the sick child (measuring child nutritional and immunisation status, identification of any disease and provision of treatment and advice), treatment of tuberculosis and case management of STDs. Most of the services in the minimum package could be delivered by nurses and midwives. The cost of the minimum clinical package was estimated to be around US$8 per person annually in low-income countries. When the cost of selected public health interventions was added, the cost rose to around US$22 in low-income countries and US$25 in middle-income countries.

In low-income countries, governments are actually spending an average of US$5 per person annually for health, and in the poorest countries, around US$2. Current proposals for funding essential health care for the poor include, cost-recovery schemes (such as charging for services in hospitals), unsubsidised health insurance for middle- and upper-income groups, encouraging competition among providers and prepayment to care-providing institutions, plus disseminating information on providers' prices and insurers' products. Other proposals include setting limits on compensation of physicians and hospitals, greater reliance on non-government organisations and the private sector, decentralisation of government services, and competitive procurement of drugs, equipment and non-medical services. Such health reforms/schemes are proving difficult to implement, unless there is strong political will in a country, and serious commitment to the poor. Even if the right package(s) are identified who can deliver them effectively?

As health services deteriorate, fewer patients use them, fewer resources are allocated to them and the whole system slides downwards. While there are many essential things which rural and urban households/communities can do – and have done – to improve their own health, there are specific things which remain the responsibility of the health services, such as immunisation of young children and pregnant women, and diagnosing and treating tuberculosis. The kind of health facilities and outreach services which are undergoing such a rapid deterioration at present are exactly those which the poor and vulnerable most need. The next sections look at how poorer countries are trying to finance essential packages and services for the poor.

9.3 HOW DEVELOPING COUNTRIES ARE TRYING TO RECOVER HEALTH COSTS

PUBLIC HEALTH EXPENDITURE

NATIONAL COST RECOVERY RATES

COUNTRY (DATE OF STUDY)	% of recurrent expenditure
China 1988	36.0
Côte d'Ivoire 1986	3.1
El Salvador 1990	4.0
Ghana 1990/1	5.6
Indonesia 1985/86	10.0
Kenya 1993	2.1
Lesotho 1991/2	9.0
Mali 1986	2.7
Mauritania 1986	12.0
Mozambique 1992	1.0 or less
Papua New Guinea 1987	3.0
Senegal 1986	7.0
Swaziland 1988/9	4.6
Zimbabwe 1991/2	3.5

Sources: Nolan and Turbat (1993)
Vogel (1991)

In poorer developing countries total government budgets have shrunk, as well as the percentage of the budget allocated to health. For example, between 1980 and 1984, spending per capita on health fell in over 60 per cent of the countries in Latin America, while in Africa, between 1987 and 1983 it fell in 7 out of 15 countries, and in 4 out of 12 countries in South and East Asia (FAO 1990).

In poorer countries, the main way of supplementing tax-based funding of public health care has been by charging user fees in government health facilities. They are usually introduced either as part of a national health cost recovery scheme (local government may also provide some financial resources for health) or as an element of a community cofinancing approach. With either approach, experience with user fees suggests that only limited amounts of revenue can be generated for the health system, as the illustration shows (adapted from Gilson & Russell (1994)).

Can user fees really recover costs?

It is reported that cost recovery systems recover only five to ten per cent of the health budget and affect the poor most (Bazgar & Korei 1991). How much is recovered also depends on how both fees and costs are measured. The illustration above contains estimated fee revenue as a percentage of total ministry of health recurrent expenditure (spending on non-fixed items such as salaries and drugs, but not capital costs such as buildings). It suggests only a small percentage of government health expenditure is recovered through fees, and that by themselves user fees will not be able to support the full costs of providing health care.

However, cost recovery data are difficult to interpret. First, different communities in the same country may record different levels of cost recovery. Second, it depends on how recovery rates are calculated. For example, two communities may each declare 100 per cent cost recovery rates, but one may recover the full cost of all non-salary operating costs, while the other may receive only drug costs. Even at community level, additional funds are necessary to cover the full cost of health care provision. It is likely that government funding will remain the main funding source for health, unless insurance schemes can be introduced (Gilson & Russell 1994).

In some places, such as francophone Africa, people have traditionally received health consultations free, but paid for prescribed drugs. In other places, both consultation and drugs have been free, and in others, people paid for consultations but received free drugs – if there were any in stock.

9.4 USER FEES AND THE POOR

The evidence of the effect of user fees on the poor is conflicting. There are some examples of user fees placing a disproportionate burden upon the poor and, where health resources and facilities are not equitably distributed, effectively ending up as subsidising curative and urban-centered services for the better off (Van Bergen 1994). But as the following example illustrates, there are also positive examples of cost recovery schemes.

> ### From Experience
> In Uganda, where public health services had been deteriorating, a study of 12 health centres and dispensaries in four districts charging user fees revealed that users wanted qualified staff, with a humane approach, readily available drugs and other essential supplies. Only one centre raised sufficient income to meet recurrent monthly costs, excluding salaries and drugs. The first step at one centre was to restore reasonable quality services, and only then, with communities, to introduce user fees. Communities subsequently reported that they saw a big change in the services. 'The little money we pay is doing something.' Other centres had not prepared their communities for fee introduction, and even health staff did not fully understand the system. Few people used the centres and fee collection was low. Without resources the quality of services could not be raised and, with low quality care, people tended to use private health services. A minority of people resented paying fees, previous services being free and they already being government tax payers (Mwesigye 1994).

Other African experience (in the Cameroons) of a community health programme run over the past 15 years also indicates that cost recovery can work. Self funding was built in from the start. People understood that all income to the health post would be used to benefit the community. Income covered the cost of salaries, continuing education, maintenance and improvements to equipment for village health workers and village birth attendants. Salary levels of health staff, village health workers (VHWs) and village birth attendants (VBAs) were agreed at village level. VHWs, together with village health committee members, administer the locally generated funds. They know who are the poorest families and occasionally reduce or waive costs of care, or enable people to pay in installments, barter goods for money or appeal for support to a local church. Support for supervisory visits (nurses to health posts) comes from larger health centres and hospitals, and is also largely funded through cost recovery. For example, only around 30 per cent of nurses' costs and salaries are provided by overseas funding agencies (Mitchell 1996).

However, other studies have shown that when user fees for health service are imposed, there is a reduction in popular use of health services, particularly if their quality is regarded as poor. A study in Ghana in the late eighties, following introduction of user fees, showed that the rate of 6000 consultations in 1984 fell to under 2000 by 1987. Rural health facilities after 1985 showed a clear decline in their utilisation (Creese 1989).

9.5 CRITICAL QUESTION OF EXEMPTIONS FROM USER FEES

When user fees are charged, how can access to health care of the very poor and most vulnerable people be safeguarded?

From Experience

In 1975, under a government scheme in Thailand, family income from all sources was assessed by local village committees, and households with a monthly income below equivalent to US$80 were given a card, valid for three years, for free services at government health facilities. The system was popular, but some of the poor were ignorant of their right to a card, particularly urban slum dwellers, migrant workers, landless farmers, hill tribes and ethnic minorities. Additional eligibility criteria were added, such as membership of vulnerable groups, and housing conditions. By 1993, around 20 per cent of the Thai population was covered by the free card system, with coverage higher in poorer rural areas, such as in the northeast, where nearly 30 per cent of people had cards, compared to only 1.2 per cent in the capital Bangkok.

At first the card system covered free services from health centres to hospital level, but there was unnecessary use of higher level services. By 1994, card holders had first to contact their nearest health centre, being later referred if necessary. Costs of the card system rose rapidly because of higher take-up rates and by 1992, the budget covered only 62 per cent of the costs of the scheme. Part of the shortfall was funded by hospitals, using part of user-fee income to subsidise medical care for free card holders. New groups such as the elderly, disabled and children under 12 were included in the card scheme, increasing costs. By 1994 moves were underway to match the scheme's budget to real expenditure (Tangcharoensathien 1994.)

9.6 WHAT POOR PEOPLE ARE SPENDING ON HEALTH – AND DISEASE

People who are poor often spend a disproportionate amount of money on health – but it is really disease they are spending their money on. For example, they get malaria, or their children get diarrhoea, and they spend money on getting advice and medicines. They spend money travelling to health facilities. Diseases which would have been easier and cheaper to treat early, such as tuberculosis, leprosy and cancers are only taken late to seek advice from health staff. Treatment is more expensive, and poor families go into debt, use money lenders or sell assets to pay for treatment for disease.

Better investment of scarce funds would be in community-managed water supplies, construction of latrines, and production and use of more nutritious foods for young children and pregnant or lactating women. When the poor invest money and time in their own health, they can often cut their health spending, whether in the public or private sector.

What does it cost a poor household to keep healthy? The table on p. 164 may help in looking at costs in a particular place. It sets out basic needs, related items requiring money/costs, has an empty column for assessing local costs and a suggested system for rating importance of each item in terms of trying to keep healthy and avoid disease. Therefore: * means not important, ** means important, and *** means very important – for keeping healthy.

The table can be adapted to a local situation and may show that the resulting financial costs may be more than a poor household can afford. Can the list of items be further reduced? Which are the essential items/practices? Is there a way of obtaining some through bulk purchase, like mosquito nets? Is there a way of linking these needs to a credit and savings scheme? Can households buy some items in a certain order over time? These are questions to consider in a local context.

9.7 OTHER HEALTH FINANCING MECHANISMS TO SUPPORT PRIMARY HEALTH CARE

The examples which follow range from local initiatives by communities themselves at district level, to global initiatives spearheaded by United Nations agencies.

Community cofinancing

Community cofinancing means that the community plays a role in generating financial and other resources, in determining what health reforms should be introduced, and subsequently in managing the action. The cofinancing comes from elsewhere, such as central or local government, an NGO or a donor. There is community accountability and the main way of involving communities is through a health management committee at each health facility level. Committees can be directly or indirectly elected by communities, formed from other existing committees (such as development committees), or older committees can be reformed. Deciding how a community cofinancing scheme will be implemented is often the reason for setting up a committee. Committees later undertake wide-ranging responsibilities. These include use of funds, monitoring, management of finances and considering wider community needs.

CAN A POOR FAMILY AFFORD TO KEEP HEALTHY?

Basic needs	Items requiring money/costs	Local cost	Star rating
Food	Enough food for the family. Special foods for young children, pregnant and lactating women. Storage containers, fly traps. Fish ponds. Backyard gardening. Sugar, salt (for ORT).		
Water	Storage containers. Water use fees/rates. Community maintenance fund. Contribution to install water supply, e.g. pipes.		
Shelter	Roofing with no holes/leaks. Shoes (prevent hookworm). Blankets, if cold area. Plastic to keep body dry. Mosquito nets/coils. Fly wire at window(s). Plastic to keep living place dry.		
Land/money	Purchase seeds, fertiliser, tools. Fares/travel to markets. Start up for small income generation, e.g. dry fish, rear goats, sell kerosene. Start up for larger project, e.g. sell fertiliser, weaving, buying bullock, sewing machine, small shop.		
Security and human affection	Lock on door to dwelling. Condoms/natural family planning for family spacing.		
Human health	Health consultation fee. Prescription fee. Hospitalisation costs, e.g. surgery, blood. Health record books, e.g. child, mother. Delivery fees/costs. Transport costs to clinic. Vet/animal assistant fees. Prescriptions for medicine. Vaccination costs.		
Energy	Fuel for cooking food. Fuel for water boiling, e.g. ORT.		
Environmental health	Window for air in dwelling. Smoke exit, e.g. chimney, smokeless stove. Latrine. Soap, e.g. body/clothes washing.		

Funds for cofinancing schemes can come in various forms:

1 Donations from local charitable organisations, churches, local clubs, industry, philanthropists and wealthy community members. Donations can also be made in kind, such as crops, livestock, and contribution of voluntary labour, perhaps to build a water system or health centre, or to work as volunteer community health workers.

2 Fees for services, in which payments are made directly to patients/beneficiaries for services.

3 Prepayment schemes, including a variety of community-based health insurance schemes.

4 Heath tax/community levy, where all people are involved in a defined community and where there is an acceptable community leadership.

5 Credit schemes, designed to generate income for community groups, households or individuals.

6 Fundraising schemes, such as public entertainment shows, lotteries and subscription drives.

The illustration shows examples of cost-recovery rates for community cofinancing schemes.

COST RECOVERY RATES FOR COMMUNITY CO-FINANCING SCHEMES

COUNTRY	% RECOVERY RATES
Benin (Bohau Project)	100 plus
Ghana	40
Guinea	52
Guinea Bissau	32
Senegal	50
Uganda	19

Source: Knippenberg (1990)

Government grants

There are various direct government grants designed to finance primary health care, such as those given to build hospitals, health centres and clinics, or to pay health staff salaries, (communities may build clinics, then government pays the health staff). Indirect support is provided through government funding of road building. However, direct support can sometimes be undermined, such as when communities build a clinic, but government finds that it cannot afford to pay the salary of health staff, or the community finds it underestimated the recurrent costs needed to keep the health centre functioning. In Zimbabwe a mix of district taxes and user fees fund some local clinics. The industry and agriculture sectors may also establish clinics/health centres to serve their workforces.

Donor agencies

Many types of donor provide financial support to primary health care, such as UN agencies, international NGOs, bilateral country donors, national and local agencies (including NGOs) and philanthropists. Such financing is important, but sometimes it is difficult to prevent external donors from distorting locally identified health priorities in favour of their own policies and procedures. Donors themselves are experiencing financial difficulties due to the global recession. Funding sources, particularly public ones, have declined. In developing countries, if there has been heavy reliance on such funding, the effects of such cutbacks are felt keenly by poor and vulnerable groups. For example, even church health services, traditionally providing good quality health care to the poor, are now experiencing financial difficulties. Their own government subsidies are being cut, and the fundraisers back home are not able to contribute as before.

An example of global action designed to improve financing and development of primary health care, is the Bamako Initiative, a set of health reforms launched by WHO and UNICEF at a meeting of African ministers of health in Bamako, Mali, West Africa, in 1987. It aimed to revitalise the public sector health care system and to involve communities themselves in decisions about local health services and strengthening district management. It proposed new approaches to financing local health services – such as user fees, prepayment schemes or revolving drug funds – to generate funds that would be fed back into improving or extending local health services. By 1993, thousands of health centres in 30 countries (including three non-African countries) were participating in the Bamako Initiative.

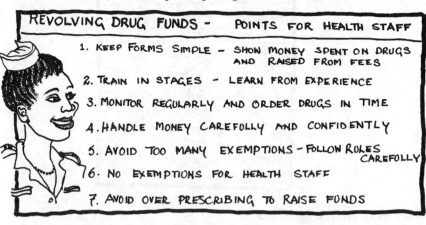

REVOLVING DRUG FUNDS – POINTS FOR HEALTH STAFF

1. KEEP FORMS SIMPLE – SHOW MONEY SPENT ON DRUGS AND RAISED FROM FEES
2. TRAIN IN STAGES – LEARN FROM EXPERIENCE
3. MONITOR REGULARLY AND ORDER DRUGS IN TIME
4. HANDLE MONEY CAREFULLY AND CONFIDENTLY
5. AVOID TOO MANY EXEMPTIONS – FOLLOW RULES CAREFULLY
6. NO EXEMPTIONS FOR HEALTH STAFF
7. AVOID OVER PRESCRIBING TO RAISE FUNDS

In a revolving drug fund (RDF) such as the Bamako Initiative, drugs are sold to patients and the money raised is used to buy more drugs. In principle, if the fund revolves successfully there will be no shortages of essential drugs. For example, in Ghana, a revolving drug fund was initiated in 1990 through the Ministry of Health. It operated in 12 districts and 100 health facilities in the Volta region where there were low levels of use of government health facilities, largely due to lack of drugs (Waddington & Asiama 1994). After four years, certain lessons have been learnt, concerning functioning and fee exemption. For example, in the Volta project, at one time

40 per cent of all drugs at government health facilities were prescribed to health workers and their families (Waddington & Asiama 1994).

Health insurance schemes

Health insurance schemes allow people to protect themselves from the high costs of curative care by making prepayments based on their personal risk of becoming ill. Insurance schemes are common in Latin America and Southeast Asia, but less common in Africa. In Brazil, for example, there is a massive health insurance scheme, while in Africa schemes are much smaller. Insurance schemes often serve people who are wage earners employed in the formal sector. However, some schemes have high administrative costs and increase the overall cost of providing care. In Latin America, governments are trying to coordinate and integrate insurance schemes in order to reduce waste and duplication, and to extend coverage to low income and other groups. Experience shows that costs may rise because insurance schemes provide incentive services which are often unnecessary, especially at the more expensive hospital level.

By introducing copayment schemes – where a user fee is paid at the time of receiving health care – as well as the cost of insurance, people can be discouraged from using health care unnecessarily. People going directly to hospital may also be charged a bypass fee. Those referred from health centres can be allowed free or lower cost access to hospitals. This can help unnecessary use of hospitals and better use of the referral system. User fees can also encourage health workers to think more carefully about the quantity and type of drugs and diagnostic tests they prescribe for patients, encouraging better use of scarce resources.

From Experience

In the Philippines a community health insurance scheme has been established as an extension to a Mother and Child Community-based Integrated Project. Activities include building basic infrastructure, preschool education and basic health services. Local women are trained for preschool day-care tasks, community organising and livelihood activities. Beneficiaries of the scheme are poor farming households with limited access to education, health services or employment opportunities. The project, operating through a central unit with 13 satellites covers 36 communities. Health services, provided by a paediatrician, two nurses and health promotors, include immunisation, monitoring of child growth and development, supplemental feeding and regular deworming for around 1000 children. Health, hygiene and nutrition education are made available for parents. Income-generating activities include food production, a bakery, weaving workshops, carpentry, welding, plantations, mushroom production and bee keeping.

The cooperative handles administration of the scheme. Hospital-based care is provided through a contract with a local hospital. The scheme will eventually serve around 2500 households, with monthly household contributions depending on family size, perhaps US$2 monthly for an individual, rising to over US$3 for a large family. These amounts are less than half the amounts that such families spend monthly on basic health care, excluding in-patient costs (Ron & Kupferman 1996).

Private practice and private health care

Where health practitioners such as retired midwives set up in private practice in rural or urban areas, they can in principle make a difference for the poor – as long as the poor can afford their fees. A few rural private medical practitioners treat a percentage of poor patients free, at least not charging for consultations. As well as western health practitioners there are many private traditional medicine practitioners who are frequently used by the poor.

From the little written about the impact of private health care in developing countries, it appears that great variations exist among doctors and other practitioners. Excellent care is provided by some, but the general picture is depressing. In particular it seems that the market forces which opened the doctors' doors in slums are determining the type and quality of the care that they provide. Services are predominantly curative. Preventive health care such as childhood immunisation and health promotion through advice on lifestyle, is uncommon. Consultations, mostly for minor ailments, are characteristically brief. The number of people seen is high – up to 100 patients a day – thus ensuring that unit costs are kept low. Standard medical practice may be ignored, with excessive numbers of drugs or overly expensive formulations being prescribed. For example, in a study of 100 private doctors, 80 treatment regimens for tuberculosis were identified. Only four of these followed the standard guidelines of WHO, and the prescribed regimens cost three times as much as the standard protocols (BMJ 1993).

The entrepreneurial approach

This includes income-generating schemes, such as renting or leasing part of someone's land, buildings and equipment in order to produce an income. It also includes *soft loans* and special assistance from banks and financing agencies to pay for profitable ventures. In some places health schemes are provided so that local industry can offer health services to employees. It includes endowment funds, where people leave instructions for money to be paid regularly to a particular cause/agent after their death. Some hospitals and health programmes offer training courses and consultancy services to generate income for their activities. Some trustees, who are members of a church, trust or group which owns or runs the NGO health project, provide or obtain financial resources to support the work.

9.8 WHAT SHOULD THE POOR INVEST IN?

Where poverty is rampant and increasing, what should the poor invest in? The household level financial costs of action to prevent disease and promote better health may be quite modest and not beyond the financial or material capacities of the poor themselves. For example, projects like building a latrine, using a mosquito net or improving early weaning foods for infants are well within their capabilities. But technical backup is required for action, such as immunisation, diagnosing and treating TB, training community members to recognise danger signs during pregnancy and childbirth, and obtaining emergency medical and surgical treatment. This

has to be financed through customary and innovative financial mechanisms, such as health insurance, and decentralised district health budgeting. Other funding is required to support district and provincial hospitals, health centres and outreach services.

Both the rural and urban poor need opportunities to generate more income so that they can put in place themselves what is needed to prevent disease and maintain good health. They need some technical guidance on their best investments for health, and much more attention is needed to microeconomics – the economics of survival at household level for people who are poor and vulnerable.

> The best financial investment for the poor is to use their assets to prevent disease, maintain health and seek timely assistance at prices they can afford.

PARTICIPATORY MONITORING AND EVALUATION

This final chapter emphasises the importance of involving the poor themselves in monitoring and evaluating their own progress out of poverty and towards better health. Principles of designing participatory monitoring and evaluation (PME) systems are outlined and a set of core indicators suggested. There are many practical examples of techniques and tools, such as visual monitoring methods useful for household level as well as to rural and urban communities. Finally, there are practical suggestions for strengthening local financial accounting and for mapping changes over time.

10.1 DESIGNING MONITORING SYSTEMS WITH THE POOR

Over the past two decades much has been learnt about participatory monitoring and evaluation. It is now accepted as an integral part of a good participatory development process, and a practical sign of more equal partnership with the poor.

The way in which monitoring fits with evaluation

A simple participatory monitoring system containing agreed indicators can be used regularly to assess progress towards agreed objectives. From time to time, additional evaluation tools (a simple survey, focus group discussions, interviews, livelihood analysis, seasonality matrix) can then be used to generate more information, both qualitative and quantitative. A deeper analysis can take place and participants can draw conclusions about progress to see if adjustments are needed. Their conclusions and recommendations are used to guide further stages of the programme. In this way, ongoing monitoring contributes to periodic evaluation as part of a participatory development cycle. The next section looks at the kinds of indicators which can be used to monitor action against poverty and for health.

10.2 DEVELOPING POVERTY-FOCUSED INDICATORS

An indicator is something used to mark progress – like a signpost on a road. It should be able to reveal whether a project/programme/group action is going in the right direction, how much progress has been achieved, and how far there is still to go to achieve objectives. Indicators help to assess and measure change. There are generally two main groups of indicators: quantitative and qualitative. *Quantitative indicators* use measurements expressed as numbers such as:

1   Percentages. A percentage means a part of something in relation to its whole, which is 100 per cent. Example: of the eggs produced during November through the income-generating project, 20 per cent (one in five) were destroyed during transport to the new market outlet.

2   Rates. It helps to think of a rate as the speed at which something occurs as well as the amount. Example: the under-five mortality rate in the most remote district increased from 20 per 1000 live births to 30 per 1000 live births in the two years when rainfall was scarce.

3   Ratios. These take a particular unit and relate it to actual or potential users. Example: the ratio of literacy teachers to adult learners was increased from 1/40 (one teacher to 40 learners) to 1/30 through community contributions which enabled the hiring of an additional teacher.

Qualitative indicators relate to quality and standard, such as quality of coffee produced by a remote indigenous mountainous community, the standard of shirts produced following tailoring training for widows who care for their grandchildren orphaned through AIDS or the quality of participation in a community project.

As well as two main groups of indicators there are nine main types, each serving a different function:

Nine types of poverty-focused indicators

Indicators of availability

These show whether something exists and whether it is available. For example, the percentage of poor rural villages with primary schools or village teachers based in the villages or visiting them regularly.

Indicators of relevance

These show how relevant and appropriate something is, such as using locally made metal tongs to hold the urine of a pregnant woman over a fire to boil to see if it contains protein (a sign that she needs special care).

Indicators of accessibility

These show whether something is actually within reach of those who need it. For example, the number of urban slum families who take out low-interest loans to start new enterprises such as tailoring or small trading.

Indicators of utilisation

These show whether something made available is actually being used for that purpose. For example, the percentage of chickens owned by poor families which are vaccinated by locally trained veterinary assistants.

VACCINATED
CHICKS

CHICKS
NOT VACCINATED

Indicators of coverage

These show what proportion of people who need something are actually receiving it. For example, the percentage of urban slum households who purchase meals from low-cost restaurants or food cooperatives.

Indicators of quality

These show the quality or standard of something, such as the ability of communally constructed sea defences to withstand the onslaught of flooding from a typhoon.

Indicators of effort

These show how much, and what, is being invested to reach objectives. For example, the amount of debt a western industrialised country writes off for a developing country.

Indicators of efficiency

These show whether resources are being put to best use to achieve objectives, such as number of cases of personal household violence for which low-cost legal aid is sought to bring charges.

Indicators of impact

These show whether inputs are really making any difference. For example, the percentage of arable land owned by a wealthy minority three years after introduction of land reform in a country. How much arable land do the poor own or have access to?

Sometimes programmes or projects are started withour clear indicators. In this case, they can be built in during a periodic evaluation of progress.

Selecting indicators relating to poverty and health

In selecting which indicators to use, three questions are useful about each indicator: Is it feasible? Is it important? Is it practical? Some indicators are more suited to monitoring poverty and health at national and provincial levels. Others can be adapted for use at district level, and further adapted for use at community and household level. The potential list of indicators relating to poverty and health could be several hundred long, but a shorter list of key indicators, such as those given in Appendix B, is more useful.

10.3 HELPING PEOPLE IDENTIFY AND USE THEIR OWN INDICATORS

The best and most sensitive indicators are often those which communities and households suggest themselves. For example, the very poor in India suggested the following indicators: number of households which eat more than twice a day; families too poor to eat their own livestock products, e.g. milk; and families which have to sleep in the same place as their livestock. By using locally identified indicators the poor themselves are put at the centre of monitoring progress against poverty and for health.

In Chapter 5 participants identified their basic needs and simple indicators for monitoring their own progress towards fulfilling those needs. More recently, in an integrated rural development project in mountainous Papua New Guinea, this approach was used during a district training for volunteer village workers and peripheral health service staff. Using an empty locally made blackboard to create an average village family, the following picture emerged, showing needs and therefore types of simple indicators required.

> The best indicators are identified by the poor themselves

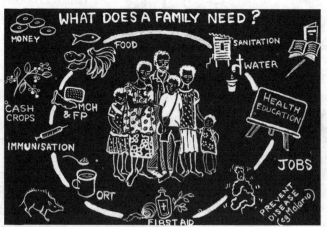

The indicators selected to monitor progress included:

- number of households with access to safe water and having a good drainage system;
- number of households constructing and using correctly a pit latrine, and burning or burying their rubbish;

- number of women with women's health record books (newly introduced by the government), and pregnant women who had specific danger signs (indicating need for special attention and care during pregnancy and childbirth);
- number of mothers preparing improved weaning foods from local foodcrops;
- percentage of eligible children completely immunised, and who were suffering from some degree of malutrition (using a simple mid-arm circumference measuring strip);
- number of mothers who could make correctly and were using home-based oral rehydration fluid ('sugar water');
- births and deaths during a particular month;
- number of deliveries in the village or the health centre;
- number of cases of sickness and people referred that month;
- families correctly using mosquito nets; and
- couples using family planning and spacing.

Indicators for tracking progress in growing and marketing food and cash crops were also suggested, along with introduction of fish ponds, community projects (clinics, roads and meeting halls), sources of family income, ownership of livestock and current prices of local essential commodities, such as kerosene and salt (see also 'Community Monitoring Board' on p. 182).

10.4 MONITORING IMPLEMENTATION OF THE PLANS

A household business plan for monitoring change

Poor families produce individual household business plans (simple line drawings) showing their circumstances, needs and plans for change. This might include renovation/alteration/extension of an existing dwelling (to include bathroom area, perhaps, or latrine, barns, livestock shelters and animal pens), or where a family plans to dig a well or construct a rainwater catchment system with tanks of metal/cement. The plan may include backyard gardening, a fish pond, production of vegetables and fruit, and livestock production such as poultry and pigs. Environmental factors are considered as well as economic and socio–cultural factors.

The top illustration on p. 176 is from a Viet Namese project where a traditional Viet Namese ecosystem approach has been revived, based on an interlocking and interdependent system using solar energy and re-use of waste products. It involves infrastructural improvements, backyard gardening, acquaculture and animal husbandry, through which are produced vegetables, pulses, tubers, fruit, poultry, eggs and fish for human consumption. Fodder from food production is fed to animals and fish. Animal wastes are used as organic fertiliser for garden and fish feeds, and pond water for growing food.

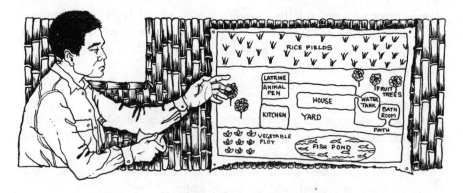

Task monitoring tools

Implementing a plan requires that various tasks be carried out by various people. A *task monitoring sheet* shows what tasks need to be carried out and when, according to the 12 months of the year. At the top of the sheet/board/blackboard are the name of the project/programme as well as the group involved and the year. Six months can be shown vertically at a time, with the remaining six months shown later on another sheet or a clean board. A sheet (poster size paper/board) can be made for each area of programme activity, which might include projects like installing community-managed water supplies or growing improved local vegetables). Participants can then see whether targets are being met and whether adjustments are necessary. Variations can be made to suit literacy and numeracy levels, such as increased or exclusive use of symbols/pictures.

Farmer's own record

By keeping such a record, a farmer can assess the benefit of a new technique. He/she may want to assess cost benefit, the amount of time/labour used, whether resources needed were accessible or whether the products were of a good standard. A tally stroke system is used to record time spent doing specific tasks on the new plot compared to the old one. For example, in preparing the ground, planting, weeding, spraying and harvesting. Each tally stroke represents a half day spent on the particular task.

·FARM RECORD		Control Plot	Test Plot
PREPARING GROUND		IIII	NHl II
PLANTING		II	III
WEEDING		NHl II	NHl
SPRAYING			I
HARVESTING		II	III

Adapted from Stephens (1988).

Monitoring group processes and participation

Participants need to monitor how many community meetings are held that year, the number of people attending, whether planned tasks were carried out on time, whether proper records are kept of community meetings and decisions, and whether the accounts are being properly maintained. Also, changes in leadership, degree of participation, and whether people achieved mutual decision-making. A simple visual tally system can also be used here.

Community forestry monitoring chart

Particular activities can be monitored by using a visual method, such as this example from a small community forestry project. It uses numbers for participants to rate their assessment of group processes, but with a little adjustment could easily use visual symbols instead of numbers for non-literate participants. One chart can cover six months.

COMMUNITY FORESTRY MONITORING CHART	NURSERY	TREE PLANTING	FERTILIZER	EXTERIOR SUPPORT	GROUP MEETINGS	LOAN REPAYMENTS	FUELWOOD	FODDER	FRUITS	SOIL IMPROVEMENT	VISITORS
JANUARY	3	3	4	5	4	2	2	3	4	3	1
FEBRUARY	3	4	4	4	4	3	3	3	3	4	2
MARCH	4	4	3	5	5	3	3	3	4	4	3
APRIL											
MAY											
JUNE											

GOOD 1 → 2 → 3 → 4 → 5 BAD

Adapted from Stephens (1988).

There also needs to be monitoring of participation itself, for instance of the number of participants who attend meetings, what percentage they are of total members, the average attendance at meetings, how much labour is contributed voluntarily (person/days) and participation in training schemes (type of training, number and person/days).

10.5 BASIC MONITORING OF FINANCIAL PROGRESS

Basic approaches and techniques

Basic financial monitoring at local level can be carried out in various ways. Often a monitoring sheet or ledger (large specially prepared book containing columns) contains basic information about debit (what funds go out/are spent), credit (what funds comes into the project/programme) and the balance (what funds remain at any one time). For smaller programmes an analysed cash book system is very useful. The procedure is to write down each receipt (money coming in) and payment (money going out) **twice** when it is recorded in the cash book. It is recorded **once** in a column (see illustration) for bank or cash, according to whether a cheque or cash was used to buy the item, and **once** in a column according to the type of receipt or expenses.

RECEIPTS: MARCH

Date	Description	Ref	Bank	Cash	Gifts	Project	Rent	Sundry
1/3/96	Donor		1,000 00		1,000 00			
1/3/96	Use of Car			35 00				
5/3/96	Rent		100 00				100 00	35 00
10/3/9	Sale of Shirts			8 00		8 00		
			1,100 00	43 00	1,000 00	8 00	100 00	35 00

EXPENSES: MARCH

Date	Description	Ref	Bank	Cash	Salaries	Food	Fuel	Sundry
	Budject March				800 00	500 00	250 00	200 00
2/3/96	Fuel - Car	125		50 00			50 00	
2/3/96	Salary - Macuvi	126	210 00		210 00			
5/3/96	Beans	127	114 20			114 20		
5/3/96	Stamps	128		23 50				23 50
7/3/96	Stationery	129		45 00				45 00
7/3/96	Salary - Nyanga	130	250 00		250 00			
			574 20	118 50	460 00	114 20	200 00	68 50

Adapted from Maclay (1996).

It is this process of analysing each receipt or expense into different types, such as food or fuel, that gives the system its name (Maclay 1996). All payments using cheques are kept separate from payments using cash. This makes it easier to check each month that the total on the bank statement agrees with the total (in the cash book) of receipts in the bank column, less expenses in the bank column.

Normally, it is more difficult to balance the amount of cash in the cash tin (petty cash) with the balance in the cash book because the number of transactions is usually greater. However, this is more easily done by checking

> **BANK BALANCE = bank column receipts less bank column expense (as long as all cheques have been cleared).**

that the total in the cash tin agrees with the total (in the cash book) of receipts in the cash column, less expenses in the cash column.

Preparing the periodic or final accounts

One major advantage of this accounting system is that the receipts and expenses are sorted immediately according to their type **when recorded** in the cash book – not several months later, such as when accounts have to be presented to a meeting. Too often the reason for a particular expense six months ago can be forgotten, but if it is recorded, it will immediately save time and avoid problems. When accounts are prepared, say for a financial meeting, the totals can be typed out (see below), without having to sort each transaction again. All the columns are added up at the end of each page. Check that the total of the bank and cash columns is equal to the total of all the analysed columns before going on to the next page.

In the example given, there are also columns for the date, description and reference number (for the cheque, invoice or bill). These details are always necessary for a well-organised accounting system. You may also find it useful to write the budgeted amount available for each expense in red above each column. This will remind you if the total in a particular column is getting close to the amount available in the budget. You will then be aware of the situation immediately, instead of months later when you prepare the accounts.

The illustration shows how accounts for the period would be presented to a meeting.

Adapted from Maclay (1996).

Financial monitoring where literacy and numeracy skills are low

Where there are few, if any literacy or numeracy skills, visual accounting monitoring charts can be used. Financial information is then summarised regularly (monthly or quarterly, perhaps) in an exercise book by a nominated person. This information can then be shared with those at district or national levels, and with NGOs. The example at the top of p. 180 shows a local project accounting summary for a tailoring project.

TAILORING PROJECT	ACCOUNTING SUMMARY			
MONTH: September YEAR: 1997	REPORTER: Anna			
ITEM BROUGHT FORWARD		DEBIT	CREDIT	BALANCE
				250
Sale of 20 school uniforms			100	350
Purchase of cloth		150		200
Purchase of buttons		20		180
Sale of 10 trousers			50	230
Repair of sewing machine		50		180
Sale of 40 boy's shirts			100	280
Total Balance				280

COMMENTS:

DATE: 2/9/97   SIGNED: ___ CHECKED: ___

Monitoring whether profits are being equitably shared

The example below shows how cash profits were distributed over a six-month period in a project where six women from poor households raised ducks. The chart also shows the level of monthly production, such as how many eggs were produced, sold consumed and damaged. At the bottom is the monthly balance of *net income* raised through the project. The chart can be adapted to fit many other types of activities.

DUCK PROJECT							
DISTRIBUTION OF EGGS AND CASH PROFITS		JAN	FEB	MAR	APR	MAY	JUN
MONTHLY PRODUCTION:		1295	1341	1348			
MONTHLY SALES:		1065	1065	1093			
Sofiah	⊘	60	60	60			
	$	2·60	3·60	3·60			
Hamza	⊘	24	36	36			
	$	4·04	4·56	4·56			
Maimunah	⊘	48	60	48			
	$	3·08	3·60	4·08			
Maziah	⊘	60	60	60			
	$	2·60	3·60	3·60			
Noor	⊘	24	36	24			
	$	4·04	4·80	5·04			
Amina	⊘	12	24	24			
	$	4·52	5·04	5·04			
TOTAL EGGS CONSUMED		228	276	252			
BROKEN, DAMAGED EGGS		2	-	3			
TOTAL NET INCOME		$42·60	$42·60	$43·72			

Adapted from Stephens (1988).

10.6 MONITORING CHANGES OVER TIME

Mapping can show changes over time

Various types of mapping can be used to monitor changing circumstances in urban and rural poor communities. Maps have been drawn on plaster, mud walls, whitewashed wood, fabric, card or strong plastic and paper. The maps drawn on the ground or in sand are good for appraising and analysing a situation, but something more permanent may be required for participatory monitoring. Maps inside a building usually last much longer than those in the open air, but maps drawn/painted on external walls have also been successful in mobilising communities and monitoring action. The following example shows a farming community before a development project started (1) and two years later (2).

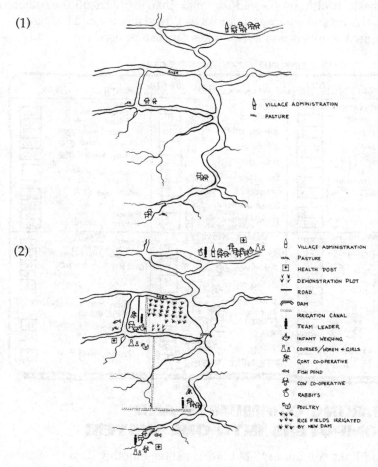

It may be important to monitor relationships between changes, such as food intake during harvest time compared to reduced intake during lean agricultural periods. (See illustration showing relationship between seasonality and disease on p. 27.)

Community monitoring boards

A community monitoring board can enable collective monitoring of progress in a rural community or an urban neighbourhood. For example, in a Malaysian district community health project community monitoring boards were prepared and used by communy health and development committees. The format was painted permanently on to the board (size of a medium blackboard) but the information, which changed monthly, was drawn in with chalk. Each month the information was transferred into a specially prepared exercise book. When the district health team visited (sometimes quarterly), they copied the quarterly information into their own record book. In this way a regular monitoring system was put in place, stretching fom participating communities to participating district extension officers. The illustration shows demographic changes, vital events (births, deaths) a basic health profile, educational changes, agricultural/other extension activities and community projects. Where literacy and numeracy skills are limited, symbols and tally strokes can also be used.

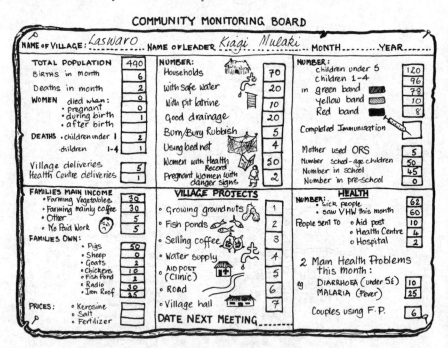

COMMUNITY MONITORING BOARD

10.7 LINKING COMMUNITY AND COMPUTERS INTO ONE SYSTEM

This method links community field worker three-monthly data collection with a microcomputer system at district level. The information is collected in the form of quarterly sequential data summaries. Information collected may relate to demographic changes, vital statistics, agricultural inputs, production outputs and other project information. These summaries can show trends and achievements, and identify problems. The information required by the various potential users is then made available to them in an appropriate form. Such a system can also be linked to a community monitoring board system, but any system which contains a computer element can be undermined where electricity supplies are unreliable as it may precipitate lost data or spoiled computers.

The illustration is adapted from a system developed in rural areas of Nepal. The objective was to monitor children aged 0–5. Every three months a set of information was collected. This enabled the villages to see whether they were making progress and programme managers, who entered the summarised information on a computer, to look at the overall picture in the area.

QUARTERLY CHILD HEALTH MONITORING (0–5 YEARS) FILE NAME: N.E.P.						
YEAR	1997	1997	1998	1998	1998	1998
MONTHS	7-9	10-12	1-3	4-6	7-9	10-12
FAMILIES IN SURVEY	22	95	60	186	100	220
% USING FAMILY PLANNING	4.5	4.10	5.5	5.0	6.5	6.5
BIRTHS LAST QUARTER	2	5	2	4	6	5
DEATHS LAST QUARTER						
CHILDREN 0-35 MONTHS WITH 3 IMMUNISATIONS						
CHILDREN 0-59 MONTHS MALNOURISHED (RED ARM BAND)						

10.8 ASSESSING TECHNICAL AND OTHER SUPPORT

Development activities often involve support and technical advice from agencies and extension pesonnel. This should also be monitored at community level for factors such as frequency and type of visit, length of visit and community estimation of its usefulness. Some appraisal methods have used a variously sized circle or dot to indicate community assessment of inputs from personnel such as credit officers, health workers, veterinarians, home economists, literacy coordinators and women's development workers and agricultural extension staff.

This chapter has stressed, above all, the importance of involving the poor themselves in monitoring and evaluating their own progress out of poverty and towards better health. Some examples of useful techniques and tools have been outlined. There are many more which may be in use, or need to be developed.

AFTERWORD

This book has looked at ways in which poverty affects the health of people who are poor and vulnerable. It has acknowledged that poverty springs from both deep and shallow roots, and that to pull out some deep roots requires action by nations collectively and at country level. For action against shallow roots, there is much that can be done in districts, communities, households and workplaces to combat poverty and improve health. A first step is to assess through participatory approaches what types of poverty and ill health exist in a particular place, and what action is needed. A next step is to work out what resources – human, financial and material – are available and what other support is needed. A third step is to ensure that new combinations of approach and content developed for action are integrated, though various sectors such as employment, agriculture and health may need to take the lead depending on circumstances. Underpinning any action must be commitment to working with representatives of the poor and vulnerable as partners, respecting their local knowledge and accelerating their opportunities to move out of poverty with dignity to achieve more satisfying and healthy lives.

The book has emphasised why, without abandoning focus on community, more attention must be given to the missing link – the household level and the workplace, where people live and work. Many factors have combined to undermine traditional survival and coping patterns of the poor, such as environmental degradation, inequitable land ownership and the flood of migrants to urban areas. In both rural and urban areas the pace of change has been so rapid that the poor have been left with the ill-fitting remnants of previous survival patterns. It is time to blend traditional knowledge elements with modern ones, not as in 'putting back the clock' which cannot be done, but going forward on two fronts.

One is broad and involves measures such as controlling environmental degradation, reducing conflict and violence, and increasing the creation of work and economic opportunities. The other is more narrowly targeted. It is the household and workplace, where people need to screen the environment for hazardous elements and practices damaging to their health and wellbeing. Action, built on understanding of local culture and values is required to ensure that basic needs are met and elements and practices damaging health are dealt with. A combination of different types of action must be designed so that each enhances the action of the other, such as: income-generation activities accompanied by introduction of health insurance schemes plus innovative education approaches to reach children and adults who are poor, or improved food crop production accompanied by child growth monitoring and improved domestic hygiene and cooking practices.

Many useful approaches and tools for such action lie scattered across many sectors and are described in publications, newsletters, and various unpublished materials. This book has drawn some of these together to share with a wider audience. Stronger networks of sharing can help to shape action against poverty and for better health. In this way a richer harvest can be reaped by and for those who are poor and vulnerable. What happens in the household and workplace determines the level of health and wellbeing of the poor, and this in turn determines whether they can work and how they can, with support, construct their own paths out of poverty. The challenge is to implement such approaches and the time for action is now.

APPENDIX A

POVERTY PROFILE FOR ACTION AGAINST POVERTY AND FOR HEALTH – SUGGESTIONS FOR STRUCTURE AND KEY QUESTIONS

Introductory section

The two to three page introductory section needs to:

1   Outline the purpose of the poverty profile, which might be to prepare for work in district/local participatory poverty assessment or as a case study during a workshop.

2   Link to previous poverty-focused information in that particular place, such as community/household surveys.

3   Mention current national/district/local policies and strategies against poverty and for health.

4   Summarise the results of the poverty profile, such as the findings and conclusions and recommendations for action against poverty and for health which emerged from the participatory poverty assessment/case study/workshop exercise.

5   Outline the process used during the participatory poverty assessment activities or preparation of case study/workshop, and mention materials, approaches and techniques used, and people involved in creating the poverty profile.

Identification and description of poorest and most vulnerable people/households/ communities in that place

This section of the poverty profile identifies who and where are the poorest and most vulnerable population groups, and what are their characteristics. There are key questions and related sub-questions. (The listing generally follows the pattern used to list poverty-focused indicators).

Demography, dependency and vulnerability – who and where are the poor and what are their characteristics?

1   Has a poverty line been established? If so, what are its upper and lower limits? How wide is the income gap between rich and poor? What is the pattern of poverty distribution, for instance what per centage of the rural/urban population are below the upper and lower poverty lines?

2   How did people become poor. Were they born into poverty or did they perhaps become poor because of natural or man-made disasters like droughts, floods, typhoons or war? Who are the poorest of the poor and why (are they female-headed households, widows, disabled people, the chronically sick, displaced people, refugees)?

3   What are the characteristics of the rural, peri-urban and the urban poor? What are the main differences between the three types of poor?

4 Do the poor migrate within the country or out of the country? What are the reasons for such migration? If the families stay behind, how do they manage to support themselves?

5 Which are the poorest regions/provinces/districts/parts of district, and what are their characteristics? Are they perhaps more remote, more prone to flooding or most affected by degraded crop land?

6 How does poverty relate with gender, racial and ethnic characteristics? Who are the poorest women? What are the main causes of their poverty? How do they support themselves and their dependants? What is the average family size of the poorest and most vulnerable families?

7 Are there minority and/or indigenous population groups affected by poverty? If so, what are the causes of their poverty? Are they among the poorest of the poor? Are they among the most vulnerable?

8 What are the main poverty trends in the country/province/district? What methods are being used to monitor poverty trends? Have poverty-related indicators been identified, and if so at which levels (national, district, community)?

Economy, labour and employment – what are the socio–economic and employment characteristics of poor and vulnerable groups?

1 What are the main sources of income of the poor? What proportion of poor rural/urban households have an annual income less than the defined basic national minimum? What percentage of households have a single income source?

2 What type of assets (land/house/products/livestock) do the poor own? How often and why do they have to sell those assets? What type of assets do they sell first and to whom?

3 Of those who are poor, what proportion are not engaged in productive employment, such as agriculture in a rural area or waged employment or self employment in an urban area? What percentage have only seasonal employment?

4 What percentage of the poor who are employed receive wages below the minimum wage? What volume are caught in a trap of minimally paid labour and or/bonded labour?

5 What percentage of the waged labour force are female?

6 What percentage of female-headed households are below the poverty line?

7 What is the gross domestic product (GDP) of the country? What is the average GDP growth rate? What is the GDP per capita?

8 What volume of development financing is provided by external development aid in that country/province/district?

Land, agriculture and livestock – how does access to productive land and agricultural inputs effect the poor?

1 What percentage of fertile land is owned by which section of the population? What percentage of the poor are landless? If needed, are there policies/plans for land reform?

2   What is the population density in relation to agricultural land? How does this relate to the local livelihood system, such as quality of land or availability of irrigation?

3   What is the percentage of the economically active population engaged in agriculture?

4   What percentage of people in rural areas are engaged in non-agricultural activities?

5   Are agricultural households receiving services of rural extension workers? If so, how often and how useful are they?

6   Are rural households receiving credit, and if so from what sources?

7   Are rural households using agricultural inputs such as fertiliser, improved seeds and farm machinery/tools?

8   Have there been changes in livestock species/units owned by the poor? Do the poor have access to livestock foods/medicines/veterinary services?

9   What is the contribution of agriculture to the GDP? What percentage of the economically active population are engaged in agriculture? What is the per capita agricultural GDP?

10 If a large amount of outputs of poor households are home-consumed, such as food crops or fetching of water, how is their contribution as non-traded goods and activities being calculated?

11 What is the average wage of an agricultural labourer? How does that wage relate to the price of a staple food, local cost of clothes, cooking utensils, fertiliser, school fees and health clinic fees in relation to purchasing power of a poor household?

12 Are households dependent on agriculture receiving a low return for their work day that is lower than poorly paid non-agricultural workers?

Organisational strength for popular participation – are the poor being able to mobilise against poverty?

1   What number and types of rural/urban organisations exist which involve the poor? What is the size of these organisations? What volume of financial capital is raised by them? From what sources do they receive support?

2   What financial services exist for poor households, such as banking systems for the poor, local credit and savings schemes? Are there national policies and schemes to promote access to formal credit for the poor? Do lending policies of agricultural banks enable loans to the poor?

3   Are there local informal lenders (money lenders) meeting credit needs of the poor? What are their interest rates and conditions of loan? Do they preserve dependency by the poor on the lender?

4   Are rural/urban organisations involving the poor represented at district/provincial/national levels?

5   To what extent are organisations of the poor reliant on extension workers/staff paid by government/NGOs?

6   What examples are there of spontaneous self help by the poor, such as low-cost restaurants? What is the potential for building onto what the poor have organised for themselves?

Food security and nutrition – how can the poor avoid the hunger and malnutrition which undermines efforts to move out of poverty?

1   What is the recommended daily calorie intake in the country?

2   What percentage of the poor fall below this minimum nutritional requirement?

3   Have measures been taken to promote food security for the poor, and if so what are they? Examples might be: subsidised food prices, fair-price shops, food banks or ration cards.

4   What type of marketing systems are in place for sale of food and other products? Is basic food readily available and do the poor pay a fair price for food?

5   Which are the important goods in the consumption basket of the poor? These might include: dietary staples such as rice or maize and fuel, kerosene or soap?

6   What percentage of household expenditure is spent on food?

7   What are the main nutritional problems of the poor and vulnerable groups, particularly affecting children under five years of age and pregnant and lactating women?

8   What is the percentage of children under five years suffering from malnutrition, and what percentage are acutely malnourished?

9   What percentage of school-age children are below recommended weight-for-height or weight-for-age?

10   What is the iron-deficiency rate for women 15–49 years, and for pregnant women?

11   What is the relationship between the main food and nutrition problems of the poor and their socio–cultural and economic characteristics?

12   What is the status of the government food stock to meet a food gap?

Education and communications – what access are the poor getting to literacy and numeracy, and to modern communications systems?

1   What is the adult literacy rate (male/female)?

2   Is access of children to primary education protected by compulsory education laws, and if so are they enforced?

3   What is the primary school enrollment rate? What is the ratio of boys to girls entering primary school? What percentage of primary school entrants complete primary education?

4   For children in remote areas, and/or from minorities, are there special educational strategies to reach them, such as mobile teachers?

5   How many primary schools require upgrading in order to function effectively?

6   What percentage of poor households cannot pay school registration fees or buy school uniform?

7   What adult literacy and numeracy activities are available to the poor and vulnerable population?

8   What percentage of poor households own radios? What percentage have electricity inside their dwellings?

9   What access do the poor have to public roads and public transport. What is the availability of roads in remoter areas? Are there affordable fares?

Vital rates and basic health information – what factors characterise the health and wellbeing of the poor?

1   What is the life expectancy (male/female)?

2   What is the birth rate? What is the death rate?

3   What percentage of rural/urban households have access to safe drinking water? What is the average time and distance necessary to fetch water by a local poor household?

4   What percentage of rural/urban households use a hygienic disposal system for human excreta?

5   What are the five main causes of mortality and morbidity in that country/district/area? How do they relate to the poorest and most vulnerable groups?

Health, expenditure, infrastructure and manpower – what is available for the poor, and can they get it?

1   What percentage of government social expenditure is on health? What is the per capita government expenditure on health?

2   What percentage of government spending is devoted to primary health care services?

3   What factors influence access of the poor to health and social services? These might include distance, travel costs, quality of available services or cost of medicines.

4   Do health care financing arrangements exist to enable access of the poor to health care, perhaps through exemption from user fees? Is there any evidence that the poor are getting poorer by having to pay for health care?

5   In what way does the private sector contribute to meeting health needs of the poor? Is there any law to compel the private sector to address any health needs of the poor?

6   What regulations exist to guide development of private health practice?

7   To what extent have health workers (volunteer community health workers, health professionals) been used as agents of change in mobilising the poor against poverty and for health?

Safe motherhood, and newborn and child care – what factors undermine the chances of poor women and young children?

1   What is the maternal mortality rate? What are the perinatal, infant and under-five mortality rates?

2   What percentage of pregnant women are receiving minimally defined ante-natal care, such as three visits during pregnancy? What percentage of pregnant women are immunised with tetanus toxoid?

3   What is the iron deficiency rate in pregnant women?

4 What percentage of women have trained assistance at delivery from health staff or trained community birth attendant?

5 What are the main causes of maternal and newborn mortality among low-income women and infants?

6 What percentage of the newborn have a birth weight of at least 2500 gm?

7 What percentage of low-income household infants aged one year are still exclusively breastfeeding?

8 What percentage of low-income household children aged 12–23 months are fully immunised according to national policy?

9 What is the contraception prevalence rate? Are community-based contraceptive distributors available to low-income households? Are contraceptives free/accessible to the poor?

10 What is the abortion-related death rate? Do low-income women have access to safe abortion services?

Other health and social indicators

1 What percentage of low-income families have adequate dwellings? Have standards been identified for basic shelter quality for the poor? Are there low-cost housing schemes/ loans available to the poor?

2 Do government policies and strategies exist which target benefits towards ethnic and/or minority population groups?

3 What measures have been taken/are planned regarding provision of social safety nets for poor and vulnerable groups?

4 Are any types of social security systems functioning which are not funded by the government?

5 What is the number and type of industrial accident among lowest paid workers?

6 What is the number of drug and alcohol-related convictions among lowest socio–economic groups?

7 How does the level of homicides affect low-income groups through deaths or convictions?

8 What is the likely percentage of population that may be infected by HIV by the year 2000? How many AIDS cases are there at present? How many AIDS-related deaths have occurred to date?

9 How many AIDS orphans are there likely to be by the year 2000? How many AIDS orphans are there at present in the country/district/local area?

10 What kinds of home-based care initiatives have been developed for households affected by HIV and AIDS?

11 What is the estimated number of street children (both who live and work on the street and who work on the street)?

12 Which development sectors are most involved in action against poverty, and what have they achieved? These might include: trades unions established, social safety net set up, extension workers trained for community work, community organisations established.

13   Are there existing projects/programmes (run by government/NGO/CBO) which work successfully for the poor likely to be sustainable and replicable?

14   Which are the main partners/collaborators with government in relation to policies, strategies and action against poverty in the country/province/district?

15   Which are the most effective health-related projects that have had an effect on the poor? Can they/have they been scaled up and applied on a larger scale?

16   How likely is it that social safety nets/welfare programmes to benefit the poor will be sustainable? Is there a functional system of tax collection to generate revenue for such programmes?

17   What practices which can be considered corrupt are complicating development efforts to benefit the poor (this will include those relating to foreign donors, national officials, provincial, district or local officials and leaders)? What can be done to make any impact on this type of problem?

18   Have there been natural hazards or man-made disasters recently that have particularly affected the poor? What action is being taken to prevent the impact of future similar hazards and disasters?

19   What unintended effects of development have had a negative effect on the poor? This might include tourism which can create employment but can also undermine family life and increase sexually transmitted diseases.

20   Is there positive targeting of poor districts/areas by the government? If so what factors influence whether they will benefit, for instance what are the motivations of local politicians? How have the local poor benefitted from schemes like food for work programmes?

Environment, degradation and pollution – which are the main environmental factors affecting the poor?

1   What percentage of fertile land under cultivation is being affected by degradation? Are there irrigated areas falling out of production? What access do small farmers have to irrigation and drainage?

2   What percentage of forested areas have been lost during the past decade? Are there local schemes to reforest such areas? If so, how do they involve or affect the poor?

3   What percentage of poor households are using charcoal or fuel wood for cooking? What is the average distance from a poor household to fetch fuel wood?

5   What types of freshwater pollution, such as chemical pollution by industry, metals discharged during mining, unsafe disposal of human excreta or unpenned livestock, are affecting poor households.

6   What percentage of poor households are exposed to health-damaging air pollution? Are the poor being exposed to hazardous materials and wastes? What systems exist for safe disposal of domestic garbage?

7   Are the poor exposed to undue noise and traffic flow that are damaging to human health and wellbeing?

Findings and conclusions, and recommendations for action against poverty and for health

This is the most important part of profiling for poverty and health action. It needs to set out clearly.

1 What are the priority problems the poor themselves wish to take action against, how is this is to be done, and who will be taking the main responsibility for what? For instance, a village or neighbourhood development committee may delegate groups to carry out various parts of the action.

2 What are the longer-term objectives of the action, and which short-term objectives will contribute to acheiving them?

3 What simple and practical indicators do local people want to use to enable them to monitor progress of the action, and how will the monitoring take place? This might be done by using a community monitoring board, regular meetings and verbal/written reports and/or methods suitable for use by non-literate people.

4 How much will the action cost in terms of money, voluntary labour and contribution of goods such as food, building materials, and how will these costs/contributions be provided?

5 An indication of time frame, showing which action will take place, where and when. Perhaps the simple planning framework following this annex may be useful. It has been used successfully in countries in Asia and Africa.

6 What support (financial/technical/material) will be required from outside the local area, and who can provide it?

Any materials used for the case study/workshop exercise/ community planning should be mentioned in a report.

APPENDIX B

EXAMPLES OF KEY INDICATORS TO SHOW ACTION AGAINST POVERTY AND FOR HEALTH, AND WHY THEY NEED TO BE USED

Each of the main headings below precedes a list of indicators (given on the left) and the reasons why each indicator should be used (given on the right). These are the most basic indicators for assessing progress.

Demographic, dependency and vulnerability

1	Percentage of indigenous population	Often poorest. May be large (58 per cent in Guatemala in 1993 (Pan American Health Organization)).
2	Number of children under five years old as percentage population	Usually most vulnerable to poverty. Often large size (in Sierra Leone was 17 per cent in 1994).
3	Average family size	Indicates household vulnerability to food/money/land shortages.
4	Percentage of total population under 15 and over 56 years	Shows extent of more dependent/ vulnerable population.
5	Number of internally displaced persons	Links to civil unrest, conflict or natural disasters such as drought.
6	Number of refugees outside the country	Links to civil unrest, conflict.

Economic, labour and employment

1	Percentage of income accruing to each fraction of the population	Indicates trends in poverty, such as rural/urban-specific problems. Helps analysis of links between employment/wages/rural poverty. Indicates inequitable wealth distribution.
2	Percentage of population below upper poverty line rural/urban	Indicates the extent of population living in poverty.
3	Percentage of population below lower poverty line rural/urban	Shows the extent of the poorest population. Indicates most vulnerable population.
4	Number of internal migrants annually	Indicates the deterioration of rural economic conditions. Shows drift to urban areas and limited employment opportunities.

5	Workers remittances from abroad as percentage of GNP	Shows reliance on external financial inputs. Indicates the deterioration of economic conditions.
6	Percentage of economically active population unemployed	Indicates the extent of household poverty and reduced ability to access food and/or health care. Indicates likely deterioration in social fabric of society, due, for instance, to civil unrest. Indicates lack of government ability/policy to generate productive agricultural or industrial employment opportunities.
7	Percentage of female-headed households below poverty line	Indicates level and degree of household poverty. Often links to deterioration in child nutrition/health/welfare.
8	Average number of people per dwelling room	Indicates overcrowded living, for instance, in Lagos, Nigeria, it is 5.8 people per room (Population Crisis Committee 1992). Links to increased transmission of airborne and contagious diseases.
9	Percentage of villages distant from public road	Indicates isolation and neglect. Shows distance from public transport. Shows lack of access for marketing produce of poor households.

Land, agriculture and livestock

1	Average wage of agricultural labourer	Indicates extent that cash income is available to buy key food and non-food essentials, such as housing materials/medicine/school fees. To be useful it should be related to local price of a staple food, such as rice/maize/local basket of essentials, to assess purchasing power.
2	Percentage of rural households receiving institutional credit	May be small, as poor households may not be eligible for credit from bigger lenders such as the agricultural banks. The poor may use informal credit sources like money lenders, but at high interest rates, with dependency being created.
3	Percentage of households using agricultural inputs like improved seeds insecticides, farm machinery and tools	Access to inputs may link to changes in prices, distribution system or macroeconomic policies such as cutbacks/subsidy removals.

4	Population density per sq km agricultural land	Only meaningful in relation to livelihood system such as farming, plus other economic activities. An irrigated system can support 1000 people per sq km, a shifting cultivation system perhaps 20 per sq km.
5	Percentage of population owning arable land	Indicates access of rural population to productive land. Shows inequitable land distribution.
6	Arable land cultivated	May indicate inequitable landownership, for instance the wealthy might breed cattle on arable land.
7	Percentage of heads of rural households without land	Shows extent of landlessness (Nepal considers families owning less than 2.6 hectares in Terai, or one hectare in mountains as landless). Indicates household vulnerability to malnutrition/famine.
8	Number of rural extension workers per 1000 holdings/ households	Value depends on usefulness of services, for instance, whether new information and technologies result in enhanced livelihood. Frequency of visits may be better indicator. May indicate access of the poor to government services and infrastructure.
9	Number/changes in livestock species and/or units	Changes may affect economic or nutritional status/wellbeing of pastoralists.
10	Percentage of rural households using livestock foods/medicines	Access may link to changes in prices/distribution system/ macroeconomic policy/subsidy removals.

Organisational strength for popular participation

1	Number of rural organisations by type and membership as percentage economically active rural population	Shows potential capacity of poor for action against poverty, for instance through cooperatives/unions.
2	Size of capital raised by members and amount of government support	Shows level of direct government intervention/financial investment.
3	Number of apex organisations by type and degree of coverage	Indicates level of decentralisation and potential for joint action. Apex organisations might include federation of cooperatives or labour unions.
4	Degree of decentralisation and number of staff paid by government/organisations	Indicates branches at regional/district level. Shows dependency of staff on government/organisations, because of, say, local inability to employ staff.

Food security and nutrition

1	Daily calorie per capita supply (kcal/person/day) as percentage of requirement	Shows ability to access food required (in Cambodia, the daily supply was 93.4 per cent, in Bangladesh 94.2 per cent, 1988–90 (ESCAP 1993)). Indicates rural/urban malnutrition and hunger trends.
2	Percentage of population without access to adequate food supply	Shows rural/urban nutritional poverty. Shows extent of population unable to meet nutritional requirements.
3	Percentage of household expenditure spent on food	Indicates poverty level (in 1985 this expenditure in Nepal was 51 per cent in urban areas and 68 per cent in rural areas. In Ho Chi Minh City, Viet Nam, it was 80 per cent (Population Crisis Committee 1992)).
4	Percentage of children under five years suffering from malnutrition	Indicates poverty impact on vulnerable group (Thailand 26 per cent, Papua New Guinea 35 per cent, India 63 per cent in 1980–81).
5	Percentage of children under five years acutely malnourished	Indicates degree of poverty. Indicates lack of access to sufficient food to maintain child growth and health. May indicate low educational level of women regarding food preparation or dietary needs.
6	Percentage of children under five underweight as percentage all under fives	Indicates chronic undernutrition (Sierre Leone was 23 per cent in 1994).
7	Percentage of primary school children with weight-for-age or weight-for height 80 percentage, or height-for-age 90 percentage below normal	Indicates chronic undernutrition.
8	Iron deficiency rate for women 15–49 years	Indicates poor nutrition among reproductive age women. May indicate lack of access to iron supplements and lack of outreach or resources of health service.

Education and communications

1	Adult literacy rate male/female (15 years and above)	Indicates inequity in educational opportunities. Indicates gender inequality. Indicates likelihood of poverty perpetuation.

2	Percentage of children completing primary education	Indicates unsustainability for poor households. Indicates likelihood of poverty perpetuation.
3	Secondary school enrollment rate	Indicates lack of access to higher education by the poor (school attendance in Lagos, Nigeria is 31 per cent of adolescents 14–17 years, Lahore, Pakistan 32 per cent and Recife, Brazil 33 per cent in school (Population Crisis Committee 1992)).
4	Percentage of rural households with radio (per 1000 population)	Indicates access of poor to radio contact/extension/literacy programmes.
5	Percentage of urban/rural households with electricity inside house	Shows priority allocated to services for the poor. May indicate lack of financial access, perhaps cannot afford to buy light bulb/ pay bills.
6	Length and type of rural roads constructed	Shows access of remote poor to public transport, marketing, social services.

Life expectancy and health

1	Percentage of population with access to safe drinking water	Indicates key health deprivation of vulnerable groups (in Viet Nam it was 46 per cent, Papua New Guinea 34 per cent (ESCAP 1993)).
2	Percentage of population with access to sanitation	Indicates linked key health deprivation of vulnerable groups. In Indonesia it was 37 per cent, Bangladesh 6 per cent, India 10 per cent, Nepal 2 per cent (ESCAP 1993).
3	Prevalence of malaria (or dominant poverty-related disease)	Shows number of malaria cases per 100 000 population.
4	Incidence of acute enteric infections (diarrhoeal diseases)	Shows number of new cases of diarrhoeal disease within a specific period. Indicates poor household hygiene and hygiene practices, and ignorance of disease causation.
5	Prevalence of intestinal helminths (worms) among children aged 2–5 years.	Indicates lack of hygienic domestic practices and access to footwear of poor families.

Health expenditure, infrastructure and manpower

1	Government health expenditure per capita	Indicates type of health service possible. If trickle-down theory in use, poor may get very little.

2	Percentage of national health expenditure devoted to primary health care, health centres and regional hospitals	Indicates investment in services most useful to the poor.
3	Population with access to health facility within e.g. 5 km	Indicates only potential access to the poor as they may not be able to reach facility/afford fees. Shows need for mobile and other outreach services for the vulnerable groups.
4	Population per nurse/ midwife/ health auxiliary	Indicates availability of health personnel most frequently used by the poor.
5	Number of trained village/ community health workers, TBAs	Indicates strengthening of capacities of poor for health action. Indicates improved access to primary health care by vulnerable groups.
6	Districts without hospitals	Indicates weakness of health infrastructure. Shows why outreach/mobile health services needed by the poor.

Safe motherhood, newborn and child care

1	Maternal mortality rate (per 100 000 live births)	Shows lack of access by poor women/ newborn to prenatal, delivery and care after birth. Indicates neglect of women's reproductive health needs. Does not show rate for most remote poor women who die.
2	Perinatal mortality rate (per 100 000 live births)	Shows lack of access by poor households to delivery and care after birth.
3	Percentage of pregnant women receiving antenatal care from trained health care worker	May show lack of access by poor women. Does not show if poor women received minimum care.
4	Percentage of births rural/ urban attended by trained attender/location	Indicates access to safe delivery. Indicates priority placed on midwifery and TBA training.
5	Infant mortality rate (deaths of children under one year/1000 live births)	Indicates lack of access to health services or outreach health action. Indicates extent and degree of poverty (Kanpur, India, 157/1000, Recife, Brazil 122/1000, Dhaka, Bangladesh 108/1000 (Population Crisis Committee 1992).
6	Under-five mortality rate (deaths of children under five years/1000 live births)	Indicates lack of access to health services or outreach health action. Indicates extent/degree of poverty (in Cambodia it was 193/1000, Afghanistan 292/1000 in 1990 (Population Crisis Committee 1992)).

7	Percentage of newborn weighing at least 2500 g at birth	Indicates poor maternal nutrition. Indicates lack of trained birth assistance for poor women. Does not show incidence among poorest such as minority/indigenous population.
8	Percentage of children under five who had diarrhoea/fever in previous two weeks	Indicates local prevalence of diarrhoea/fever, common among poor children.
9	Number of community based contraceptive distributors (CBD)	Indicates seriousness of commitment to family planning and fertility control. Shows availability of personnel accessible to poor households (but need regular supplies, optimally free).
10	Number of abortion related deaths	Indicates lack of access to contraceptive methods. Indicates neglect of safe motherhood and reproductive health needs of the poor.

Other health and social indicators

1	Number of industrial accidents among lowest paid workers	Indicates extent of neglect for occupational health and safety for poorest groups.
2	Percentage of population estimated infected by HIV and AIDS by year 2000	Indicates extent of HIV/AIDS.
3	Number of AIDS home based care initiatives	Shows likely coping capacities of poor households.
4	Number of AIDS-related deaths to date	May indicate increasing rural household poverty among affected families.
5	Number of AIDS orphans and estimate by year 2000	Indicates extent of future provision required to tackle problem.
6	Estimated number of street children	Indicates extent of family poverty and fragmentation among poor households. Indicates size of vulnerable group in particular to physical disease/psychological disorder.
7	Number of children engaged in prostitution (social decay indicator)	Poverty and powerlessness. Child exploitation.
8	Incidence of child sexual abuse (social decay indicator)	Powerlessness, exploitation. Sexual deviance, circulation of pornographic materials.
9	Incidence of child abuse through other violence	Breakdown of family life, stress, lack of basic needs, lack of support to parents.

Environment, degradation and pollution

1 Degree of concentration of health-harming metals in fresh water
Level of lead, cadmium, mercury, pesticides in freshwater.

2 Percentage of population exposed to high concentrations of health-damaging air pollution (indoors/outdoors)
Shows extent of population affected by polluted air.
Needs to show how this affects the poor, particularly.

3 Percentage of population exposed to hazardous wastes and industrial discharges
Shows extent of population affected by dangerous pollutants.
Needs to show how the poor are affected.

4 Percentage of people served by public garbage removal service
Shows percentage of population with access to garbage disposal.

APPENDIX C

TOWARDS A DISTRICT ENVIRONMENTAL CHECKLIST

This section provides a list of key questions which need to be asked in relation to various natural resources and the environmental situation of a particular area.

Soil

1   What percentage of the land is arable?

2   What percentage of arable land is cultivated?

3   Are cultivation methods such as 'slash and burn' and burning undergrowth causing soil degradation/erosion?

4   Are chemical fertilisers in use/overused?

Water

1   What are the main fresh water surface sources (river, lake)?

2   Are there saline (salty) water sources (coastal area/marsh/mangrove swamp)?

3   Is salinity affecting fresh water sources such as wells/irrigated areas?

4   What commercial use is being made of fresh water resources?

5   What sewage is discharged into which fresh water resources?

6   Do commercial enterprises discharge waste/chemicals into fresh water sources?

7   Are other local practices such as using mercury to find gold, dumping garbage, human or animal faeces (if not intended as fish food) harming fresh water sources?

Forests

1   How large are main forested areas in the district?

2   Are forested areas natural forest or reafforested areas?

3   What commercial use is being made of forests? Is there logging or extractive harvesting (nuts, rubber)?

4   Are forested areas being cut down for agricultural purposes such as small farming/commercial farming?

5   What percentage of natural forests have been cut down during the past 20 years?

6   What reafforestation is taking place? Are there large national programmes/small-scale school projects?

Air

1   Which vehicles cause air pollution (cars/trucks/buses)?

2   Do regulations exist about maintenance of vehicle exhausts?

3   What commercial enterprises pollute the air?

4   Do regulations exist about commercial enterprise air pollution?

Minerals/metals

1   Does the district contain mineral/metal resources?

2   If so, are they being commercially extracted/unofficially extracted?

3   Do regulations exist to guide/control extraction of minerals/metals?

4   What pollution is/has been caused by extraction processes such as slag heaps?

Energy/oil/gas/coal

1   Does the district contain deposits of oil/gas/coal?

2   If so, are they being commercially/unofficially produced?

3   Do regulations exist to guide production?

4   What pollution (oil spills, coal dust contamination or disease, unreliable gas storage or conduction) has been produced by production?

Oceans and fishes

1   Have fish catching methods been harmful (over-fishing, using wasteful methods)?

2   What pollutants (untreated sewage/chemicals/garbage) are poured into the ocean?

3   What effects are evident in water/on beaches?

4   What effects are evident on fish/shellfish/sea plants?

5   Do regulations exist for sea fishing?

6   Do regulations exist for sea polluting?

7   Does processing of sea products such as disposal of fish waste cause pollution?

Livestock and poultry

1   How are urine and excreta from livestock and poultry disposed of?

2   How is the waste from animal slaughter disposed of, especially in large-scale or intensive industries/systems?

GLOSSARY

Definitions of some of the words and concepts used in this book.

ABSOLUTE POVERTY: Condition of life characterised by deprivation of elements necessary to sustain life and health, such as water, food. Also, position of an individual or household in relation to a poverty line based on the cost of a minimum consumption basket of food necessary for recommended calorie intake.

AGRARIAN REFORM: A politically fuelled movement to reshape and improve the system of use and ownership of farming land designed to promote the interests of small farmers and to improve farming systems in new and more equitable ways.

BANKING SYSTEMS FOR THE POOR: A system of financial services especially designed to increase access by low-income groups involving decentralised services, low interest rates and mobile bank officials who visit communities. Can also be 'community banks' such as revolving funds for credit and savings (ROSCAs), where community groups themselves manage the system.

BASIC NEEDS: Requirements which are fundamental to sustaining human life and health, such as physical human needs (food, water), shelter (dwelling, clothing), psychosocial and spiritual needs (social participation, human rights, religious freedom), environmental control (protection from hazardous and harmful substances) and personal and communal needs (access to land, livestock grazing, employment, social services).

BIODIVERSITY: The number and type of species in an ecosystem such as a tropical rainforest or a coral reef, where many thousands of species interact in a complex system of linked, mutually advantageous relationships.

CBO: Community-based organisations set up and run by low-income people themselves at local and community level. They provide services, assist in local problem-solving, help meet needs, strengthen local capacities and advocate on behalf of communities

CHILD PROSTITUTION: The process where children are subjected, often involuntarily, to perform sexual acts with adults in exchange for money.

COOPERATIVES: System established for production and/or distribution of goods/produce where profits are shared equally among members of the cooperative.

CRUDE BIRTH RATE: Number of infants born in a given year (or any other time period) divided by the mid-year population and expressed per 1000 population (for instance, in 1990 the world birth rate was 27/1000).

DEPRIVATION: Situation of loss and being deprived of; being without a needed or desired object or state of being.

DESTITUTION: Utterly without resources and in particular need of basics such as food, water, shelter, clothing, security, access to work or social services.

EARLY CHILDHOOD DEPRIVATION: Process whereby young children do not have access to elements which should sustain their growth and wellbeing, such as sufficient food, safe water and a stimulating environment for early psycho-emotional and intellectual development.

ENVIRONMENTAL DEGRADATION: Process by which natural or man-made environments (surrounding conditions and influences which affect normal growth or development of living things) are made worse, polluted, become diseased, are damaged or destroyed.

EQUITABLE: A process or situation characterised by a fair sharing of resources and services.

EXPLOITATION: To make unfair, unjust or selfish use of human or natural resources, usually for advantage.

FAIR-PRICE SHOPS: Commercial outlets for food and food products where the retail price is purposely lower than other outlets to enable access by low-income households and individuals.

FOOD BANKS: System where a country or programme stockpiles food at a particular place (or places) to prevent famine in case of reduction of food stocks, usually through natural hazards such as drought or flood.

FOOD FOR WORK: System where individuals and groups who are poor are employed to work, perhaps by building roads, constructing dams or irrigation systems, and instead of being paid wages are paid the equivalent in food.

FOOD SECURITY: Being in a situation of freedom from fear or danger that basic needs for food will not be fulfilled. For example providing food security may be the main focus of emergency relief operations after a drought, or it may underpin construction of a social safety net system.

HEADCOUNT INDEX: The proportion of the population whose standard of living (usually measured in income or consumption) is lower than the poverty line.

HEALTH (HUMAN): A condition of freedom from any physical or psycho-emotional illness or infirmity, and a positive state of wellbeing conducive to normal growth and development, and the leading of a satisfying existence.

HEALTH INSURANCE: A scheme which allows people to protect themselves from the costs of health care by making regular pre-payments, based on their personal risk of becoming ill, such as their age, circumstances, state of physical health and past medical history.

HIV INFECTION: Infection in the human body caused by entry of the human immuno-deficiency virus (HIV), which eventually disables the normal immune system by which the body fights disease. Transmission methods are: penetrative unprotected sexual contact (for instance without condom), sharing of unsterilised hypodermic needles (by intravenous drug users, perhaps), cutting or piercing instruments (tattooing), blood transfusion with contaminated blood, transplant with an infected organ, receiving of infected semen, contact with infected blood or body fluids if there is a break in the skin and mucous membranes, and transmission from an infected mother to her baby before, during or after birth.

INCOME GENERATION: Schemes through which people who are poor can engage in locally appropriate activities, such as growing food crops and cash crops, rearing of livestock and production of livestock products (such as milk or wool), aquaculture (like fish ponds) beekeeping, craft products (such as items made from wood or woven) or tailoring, which result in increased disposable household income.

MARGINALISATION: A process of leaving people who are poor on the fringes of society.

MATERNAL MORTALITY RATE: The number of women who die while pregnant or within 42 days of termination of pregnancy, irrespective of the duration and site of the pregnancy, from any cause related to or aggravated by the pregnancy or its management (but not accidental or incidental causes), per 100 000 live births in a given year. The *maternal mortality ratio* is the same except that the denominator used is women of reproductive age instead of live births.

MINIMAL AVERAGE INCOME: The estimated lowest average income in relation to number of people who receive an income from wage employment or other sources.

MINIMUM WAGE: The wage agreed on or fixed by law as the lowest payable to certain employees.

POVERTY: A condition of being in want of the essential elements required to sustain human life and human health. It means experiencing scarcity and deficiencies, and existing in a state of deprivation, or often of multiple deprivations.

POVERTY ASSESSMENT: An assessment which quantifies the extent and nature of poverty and identifies the policy, public expenditures and institutional issues that constrain effective poverty reduction. The assessment develops recommendations for government action aimed at reducing poverty (World Bank 1993a).

POVERTY CYCLE: A condition or process of poverty which repeats itself in the same order. For example, the children of bonded labourers may become bonded labourers themselves.

POVERTY LINE: The standard of living (usually measured in terms of income or production) below which people are deemed to be poor. It is a tool for measuring poverty, usually based on consumption or income data. There may be upper and lower poverty lines relating to levels of deprivation.

POVERTY ALLEVIATION: A process by which poverty is made easier to endure, but not necessarily one which attacks the roots of poverty.

POVERTY ERADICATION: A process which, at its best, aims to destroy completely the root causes of poverty in order to enable the poor to move out of poverty on a permanent basis.

POVERTY PROFILE: An analytical tool for rapidly and systematically revealing more clearly where the poor and vulnerable live and work, and what causes their poverty. It can also indicate how poverty varies across subgroups of a population, according to location, gender, type of economic activity and health status.

PRIMARY HEALTH CARE: Essential health care based on practical, scientifically sound and socially acceptable methods and technology made universally accessible to individuals and families in the community through their full participation and at a cost that the community and country can afford to maintain at every stage of their development in the spirit of self reliance and self determination. The global strategy for health for all by the year 2000 was based on developing country-wide health systems based on primary health care.

RATION CARD: A card which entitles the holder to a fixed allowance of food.

RELATIVE POVERTY: Refers to the position of an individual or household in comparison with the average income in a particular country. It is characterised by deprivation of opportunities, comfort, material assets and self respect regarded as normal in the community to which those affected belong.

SAFETY NET: A specially constructed network of components, legislative, financial, services, options and materials, directed towards poorer and more vulnerable groups in a particular society. It may include income transfers for those unable to work because of age or disability, or those temporarily affected by natural disasters or economic recession.

SOCIAL JUSTICE: Process within society where there are fair dealings between human beings in their relationships with each other, and where certain rights of individuals and groups are assured.

SOCIAL SERVICES: Services directed towards the betterment of social conditions, such as child welfare, support to home-based care clinics and counselling services.

VULNERABLE: Exposure and likelihood of being injured, wounded or damaged.

REFERENCES AND FURTHER READING

African Development Bank (1994a) *The African Development Bank and the Environment*, African Development Bank, Abidjan, Cote d'Ivoire.

African Development Bank (1994b) *African Platform for Action*, prepared for the Fourth Conference on Women in Senegal, 1994, African Development Bank, Abidjan, Cote d'Ivoire.

African Development Bank (1994c) *Guidelines for the Implementation of the Action Program for Poverty Alleviation*, African Development Bank, Abidjan, Cote d'Ivoire.

African Development Bank (1995) *Country Environmental Profile: Zimbabwe*, Environmental and Social Policy Working Paper, Series 2, African Development Bank, Geneva.

Aga Khan Foundation (1988) *Management Information Systems and Microcomputers in Primary Health Care*, Aga Khan Foundation, Geneva.

AHRTAG (1980) *How to Look After a Refrigerator*, Appropriate Health Resources and Technologies Action Group, London.

AHRTAG (1982) *Low-cost AIDS*, Appropriate Health Resources and Technologies Action Group, London.

AHRTAG (1983a) *How to Choose and Make a Cold Box*, (for vaccines), Appropriate Health Resources and Technologies Action Group, London.

AHRTAG (1983b) *How to Look After a Health Centre Store*, Appropriate Health Resources and Technologies Action Group, London.

AHRTAG (1987) *We Can Play and Move*, (aids for disabled children), Appropriate Health Resources and Technologies Action Group, London.

Akoth, B. (1994) 'Community action to protect the environment', *Footsteps* **20**.

Alegria, M. *et al.* (1991) 'Patterns of mental health utilization among island Puerto Rican poor', *American Journal of Public Health* **81**: 875–9.

Arnold, M. & Kanowski, P. (1993) 'New directions in forestry and agro-forestry', Issue entitled: 'How people use trees', *Rural Extension Bulletin* **2**: 3–9.

Arole, M. & Arole, R. (1995) *Jamkhed: A Comprehensive Rural Health Project*, Macmillan, Basingstoke.

Ashworth, G. (ed.) (1995) *A Diplomacy of the Oppressed: New Directions in International Feminism*, Zed Books, London.

Atkinson, S. J. & Cheyne, J. (1994) 'Immunization in urban areas: issues and strategies', *Bulletin of the World Health Organization* **72**: 183–94.

Bajracharya, P. & Bajracharya, B. (1991) *Towards Integrated Strategies for Alleviating Rural Poverty in Nepal*, International Labour Organization and ARTEP, New Delhi.

Ball, C. & Dunn, L. (1995) *Non-Government Organizations: Guidelines for Good Policy and Practice*, Commonwealth Foundation, London.

Bazgar, M. & Korei, A. (1991) *A Solid Base for Health*, World Health Forum, World Health Organization, Geneva, pp. 156–60.

Belsey, M. (1993) 'Child abuse: measuring a global problem', *World Health Statistics Quarterly* **46**.

Berry, D. J. *et al.* (1991) 'An evaluation of the national measles campaign in the new shanty areas of Khayelitsha', *South African Medical Journal* **79**.

Bhaskara, H., De Silva, D. *et al.* (1989) *Against All Odds: Breaking the Poverty Trap*, Panos, London.

Bhattaria, B. (1993) 'Nepal, a problem of governance', *People and Planet*, **2 April**: 10–13.

Blackburn, C. (1993) *Health Visitor* **7**: 254–6.

BMJ (1993) *British Medical Journal* **306**.

Bonnie, J. L. & Bishop, S. J. (1994) 'Predictors of behavioural problems in pre-school children of inner-city Afro-American and Puerto Rican adolescent mothers', *Child Development* **65**: 638–48.

Brehony, B. & Ssemulassa, M. (1992) 'Courage, compassion and care', *AIDS Action* **19**.

Broad, R. (1994) 'The poor and the environment: friends or foes?' *World Development* **22**: 811–22.

Burne, S. (1995) *Let the Dawn Come: Social Development – Looking Behind the Clichés*, Panos, London.

Campos, R. *et al.* (1994) 'Social networks and daily activities of street youth in Belo Horizonet, Brazil', *Child Development* **45**: 319–30.

Carnegie Foundation (1996) 'Mental illness: the hidden crisis in developing countries', *Carnegie Quarterly* **XLI:** 5–7.

Carrin, C. & Vereecke, M. (1992) *Strategies for Health Care Finance in Developing Countries: With a Focus on Community Financing in Sub-Saharan Africa*, Macmillan, Basingstoke.

Chan, E. K. (1990) 'A Compendium of Data on Poverty and Income Distribution', background paper for World Development Report, World Bank, Washington, DC.

Chaulagai, C. N. (1993) 'Urban community health volunteers', *World Health Forum* **14**.

Chege, N. (1995) 'Lake Victoria: a sick giant', *People and Planet* **4:** 14–17.

Chen, L. *et al.* (1993) 'Is Poverty Increasing in the Developing World?', Policy research working paper WP5 1146, World Bank.

Chester, T. (1996) 'The world's missing women', *Footsteps* **27:** 5.

CIMADE (1996) *Vol d'Organes*, Bayard, Paris (plus video, *Vol d'Organes*, available from 176 rue de Grenelle, 75007 Paris, France).

Colchester, M. (1993) 'Sustaining the Forests: The Community-based Approach in South and Southeast Asia', discussion paper, United Nations Institute for Social Development, Geneva.

Coll, A. M. (1990) 'Santé et ajustement structural', *Vie et Santé* **2:** 13–15.

Commonwealth Foundation (1995a) *Paths out of Poverty: The Role of NGOs*, Proceedings of Second Commonwealth NGO Forum, Commonwealth Foundation, London.

Commonwealth Foundation (1995b) *Report of the Second Commonwealth NGO Forum, Wellington, New Zealand*, Commonwealth Foundation, London.

Commonwealth Secretariat (1991) *Crushing Rural Poverty*, Food Production and Rural Development Division, Commonwealth Secretariat, London.

Commonwealth Secretariat (1993) *Action to Reduce Poverty*, Food Production and Rural Development Division, Commonwealth Secretariat, London.

Commonwealth Secretariat (1993a) *Strategies for Poverty Reduction*, Commonwealth Secretariat, London.

Commonwealth Secretariat (1995) *Non-government Organizations: Guidelines for Good Practice*, Commonwealth Secretariat, London.

Community Development Journal (1987) Issue entitled: 'Livestock and community development', *Community Development Journal* **22**.

Community Development Journal (1992) Issue entitled: 'Tourism and community development', *Community Development Journal* **27**.

Contact (1995a) Issue entitled: 'Financing health care', *Contact* **141** (February–March).

Contact (1995b) Issue entitled: 'District health systems: decentralizing for greater equity', *Contact* **143** (June–July).

Contact (1996) Issue entitled: 'Health financing crisis: can communities afford to pay', *Contact* **146** (December 1995–January 1996).

Creese, A. (1989) 'Economic issues in health services development', bulletin of the Agricultural Extension and Rural Development Department, University of Reading, February.

Creese, A. (1990) 'User charges for health care: a review of recent experience', *Journal of Health Policy and Planning* **6:** 309–19.

Creese, A. *et al.* (1990) 'Cost analysis in primary health care: a training manual for programme managers', World Health Organization, Aga Khan Foundation and UNICEF, Geneva.

Curtin, P. (1990) 'Migration in the tropical world', in: *Immigration Reconsidered: History, Sociology and Politics*, Oxford University Press, New York.

Davis, D. (1994) 'What makes a disaster', *Footsteps* **18:** 8–9.

Davis, I. & Wall, M. (1994) *Christian Perspectives on Disaster Management*, TEAR Fund, Teddington.

Davis, S. (1995) 'The Sahel: drought, trees and livestock', *Rural Extension Bulletin* **2**.

De Gaspar (1982) *World Hunger: A Christian Reappraisal*, World Council of Churches, Geneva.

Dickson, M. (1985) *Where There is no Dentist*, Hesperian Foundation, Palo Alto, CA.

Dorea, J. G. & Furumoto, A. V. (1992) 'Infant feeding practices among poor families of an urban squatter community', *Annals of Nutrition and Metabolism* **36:** 257–64.

Easter, C. (ed.) (1993) *Strategies for Poverty Reduction*, Commonwealth Secretariat, London.

ECLAC (1990) 'Magniyud de la obreza en America Latina en los anos ochenta', LC/L.533, Economic Commission for Latin America and the Caribbean, Santiago, Chile, 31 May.

ECLAC (1994) *Health, Social Equity and Changing Production Patterns in Latin America and the Caribbean*, Economic Commission for Latin America and the Caribbean.

ESCAP (1993) *The Regional Poverty Situation, National Policy Approaches and International Initiatives: Regional Poverty Situation, The Poverty Situation in Asia and the Pacific*, Economic and Social Commission for Asia and the Pacific, E/ESCAP/CAP/ 1, Bangkok, 28 July.

Falkenmark, M. & Widstrand, C. (1992) 'Population and water resources: a delicate balance', *Population Bulletin* 43: 2–35.

FAO (1981) *The Peasant's Charter: The Declaration of Principles and Programme of Action of the World Conference on Agrarian Reform and Rural Development*, Food and Agriculture Organization, Rome.

FAO (1983) *The State of Food and Agriculture 1982, Livestock Production: A World Perspective'*, Food and Agriculture Organization, Rome.

FAO (1988) *Women in Fishing Communities*, Food and Agriculture Organization, Rome.

FAO (1990) *Women and Agricultural Development: The FAO Plan of Action*, Food and Agriculture Organization, Rome.

FAO (1992) *People's Participation in Rural Development: The FAO Plan of Action*, Food and Agriculture Organization, Rome.

FAO (1993a) *Design of Poverty Alleviation Strategy in Rural Areas*, Economic and Social Development paper 115, Food and Agriculture Organization, Rome.

FAO (1993b) *Rural Poverty Alleviation: Policies and Trends*, Economic and Social Development paper 113, Food and Agriculture Organization, Rome.

FAO (1995) *Issues in Rural Poverty, Employment and Food Security*, Food and Agriculture Organization, Rome.

Ferge, Z. (1991) 'Marginalization, poverty and social institutions', *Labour and Society* 16: 417–38.

Feuerstein, M. T. (1986) *Partners in Evaluation: Evaluating Development and Community Programmes with Participants*, Macmillan, Basingstoke.

Feuerstein, M. T. (1993a) 'Participatory evaluation: the Patna experience', *Contact* 132: 1–15.

Feuerstein, M. T. (1993b) *Turning the Tide: Safe Motherhood, A District Action Manual*, Macmillan, Basingstoke.

Feuerstein, M. T. & Lovel, H. (1987) 'The role of livestock in community development', *Community Development Journal* 22: 174–88.

Figueirero, J. B. & Shaheed, Z. (eds) (1995) *Reducing Poverty Through Labour Market Policies*, International Labour Office, Geneva.

Figueras, A. (1992) 'Among the street children', *World Health*, **May–June**: 6–8.

Finamore, S. (1996) 'Self help finance for the poor', *Footsteps* 26.

Footsteps (1994) Special issue on TB and AIDS, *Footsteps* 19.

Fourth World (1991) *The Wresinski Approach: The Poorest Partners in the World*, Fourth World, London.

Fourth World Journal, all issues useful for reference, Fourth World, London.

Garcia, S. R. (1995) 'Lessons of the Zapatista uprising', pastoral letter 1994, Catholic Institute for International Relations, London.

Garrett, G. (1993) *Adding Health to Years: A Basic Handbook on Older People's Health*, Helpage International, London.

Ghai, D. & Hopkins, J. (1988) *Some Reflections on Human and Social Indicators for Development*, United Nations Research Institute for Development, Geneva.

Gilbert, A. & Gugler, J. (1984) *Cities, Poverty and Development: Urbanization in the Third World*, Oxford University Press, Oxford.

Gilman, R. H. *et al.* (1993) 'Water cost and availability: key determinants of family hygiene in a Peruvian shantytown', *American Journal of Public Health* 83: 1554–7.

Gilson, L. (1994) 'What price for health care?', *Health Action* 9: 4–5.

Gilson, L. & Russell, S. (1994) 'Can fees recover costs?, *Health Action* 9: 9.

Golding, A. M. B. (1995) 'Understanding and preventing violence: a review', *Public Health* 109: 91–7.

Goodman, H. & Waddington, K. (1993) *Financing Practical Care*, Oxfam Practical Guide 8, Oxfam, Oxford.

Gordon, G. & Kanstrup, C. (1992) 'Sexuality – the missing link in women's health', *Institute of Development Studies Bulletin* 23: 29–37.

Goudzwaard, B. & De Lange, H. (1986) *Beyond Poverty and Affluence: Towards an Economy of Care*, World Council of Churches, Geneva.

Government of the Republic of Zambia (1992) country report at the FAO/WHO International Conference on Nutrution, Rome.

Grudeboen, B. (1987) *Neonatal Tetanus Cases in Luanda*, Government of Luanda, Angola, Luanda.

Gunatilleke, G. *et al.* (1992) 'Rural poverty in Sri Lanka: priority issues and policy measures', *Asian Development Review* **10**: 164–98.

Gupta, N. (1994) 'Numeracy: a pre-requisite for phase out: some thoughts on developing a numeracy course', *Education Action* **1**: 10–11.

HABITAT (1996) *An Urbanizing World: Global Report on Human Settlements*, HABITAT and Oxford University Press, Oxford.

Hamburg, D. (1994) *Education for Conflict Resolution*, Carnegie Corporation, New York.

Hanson, K. & Gilson, L. (1993) *Cost, Resource Use and Financing of District Health Services: A Practical Manual*, Bamako Initiative technical report 16, UNICEF, New York.

Harpham, T. & Blue, I. (eds) (1995) *Urbanization and Mental Health in Developing Countries*.

Harpham, T. & Janer, M. (1995) *Urban Health in Developing Countries: Progress and Prospects*.

Harpham, T., Lusty. T & Vaughan, P. (1988) *In the Shadow of the City: Community Health and the Urban Poor*, Oxford University Press, Oxford.

Hata, K. (1996) 'Crediting seeds: sup-sup gardens make the difference', *Common Path*, **January:** 10.

Health Action (1993) Issue entitled: 'Health and work', *Health Action* **5**.

Health Action (1994) Issue entitled: 'Paying for health care', *Health Action* **9**.

Health Action (1995a) Issue entitled: 'Tackling poverty to improve health', *Health Action* **12**.

Health Action (1995b) Issue entitled: 'Health sector reform – coping with change', *Health Action* **13**.

Heise, L. *et al.* (1994) *Violence Against Women: The Hidden Health Burden*, World Bank discussion paper 255, World Bank, Washington, DC.

Helmer, R. (1992) 'News from the waterfront', *World Health Magazine*, **July/August**.

Helpage International (1994) *Ageways 36: Practical Age Care for Development*, Helpage International, London.

Helpage International (1995) *Older Women in Development*, Helpage International, London.

Herley, D. (1990) *Income Generation Schemes for the Urban Poor*, Oxfam development guidelines 4, Oxfam, Oxford.

Hernandez (1994) article in *The Nation* **28** (Mexican newspaper).

Hinrichsen, D. (1995) 'Requiem for a dying sea', *People and Planet* **4**: 10–13.

Holden, P. (1995) 'Making tourism more responsible', *Contact, Special Issues in Tourism* **142:** 7–10.

Hutaserani, S. 'The trends of income inequality and poverty and a profile of the urban poor in Thailand', *Thailand Development Research Institute Quarterly Review* **5**.

IFAD (1988) *Report of the Special Programming Mission to Ghana*, report 0105-GH, International Fund for Agricultural Development, Rome.

IFAD (1994) *The Challenge of Poverty: The Role of IFAD*, International Fund for Agricultural Development, Rome.

ILO (1992) 'Statistical sources and methods', *Household and Expenditure Surveys*, vol. 6, International Labour Office, Geneva.

ILO (1993) *The Incidence of Poverty in Developing Countries: An ILO Compendium of Data*, International Labour Office, Geneva.

ILO (1994a) *Employment and Population: An Inseparable Duo*, International Labour Office, Geneva.

ILO (1994b) *Indigenous and Tribal People and the ILO*, International Labour Office, Geneva.

ILO (1995a) *Gender, Poverty and Employment: Turning Capabilities into Entitlements*, International Labour Office, Geneva.

ILO (1995b) *Women Work and Poverty in Africa: Agenda for Action and the Proceedings*, International Labour Office, Geneva.

ILO/PREALC (1991a) *Banco de Datos Sobre Empleo, Remuneraciones y Pobreza*, International Labour Office and PREALC, Panama City.

ILO/PREALC (1991b) *La Pobreza en Centroamerica: Resumen Estadistico*, International Labour Office and PREALC, Panama City.

Jacobs, M. (1996) *The Politics of the Real World*, The Real World Coalition, Earthscan Publications, London.

Jaswal, I. & Gulati, J. (1992) 'Situational analysis of antenatal care practices in rural Punjab', *Indian Journal of Maternal and Child Health* **3:** 16–18.

Jayasundere, R., Series on savings and credit – 1: *The Selection of Loanees*; 2: *The Design of Savings and Credit Schemes*; 3: *The Monitoring Process*; 4: *Impact and Support*; 5: *Case Studies in Savings and Credit*, IRED – Development Innovations and Networks, Colombo, Sri Lanka.

Jazairy, I., Alamgir, M. & Panuccio, T. (1992) *The State of World Rural Poverty: An Inquiry into its Causes and Consequences*, New York University Press for IFAD, New York.

Johnson, P. (1994) *Management Support for Primary Health Care: A Practical Guide to Management for Health Centres and Local Projects*, FSG Communications Ltd, Cambridge.

Kalache, A. & Coombes, Y. (1993) 'The world is getting older: what are the implications? *The Health Exchange*, **Dec 1992–Jan 1993.**

Kaplan, R. D. (1994) 'The coming anarchy', *The Atlantic Monthly*, pp. 44–75.

Khan, A. R. (1993) *Structural Adjustment and Income Distribution*, International Labour Office, Geneva.

Khandker, S. *et al.* (1994) *Is Grameen Bank Sustainable?*

Knippenberg, R. F. *et al.* (1990) *The Bamako Initiative Primary Health Care Experience. Children in the Tropics*, International Children's Centre, Paris, pp. 184–5.

Lazo, O. (1994) 'Two faces of poverty', *World Health* **6**.

Leake, A. (1994) 'Community action and the environment', *Footsteps* **20**.

Lennock, J. (1994) *Paying for Health: Poverty and Structural Adjustment in Zimbabwe*, Oxfam, Oxford.

Le Roux, I. M. & Le Roux, P. J. (1991) 'Survey of the health and nutrition status of a squatter community of Khayelitsha', *South African Medical Journal* **20:** 500–03.

Lipton, M. & De Kadt, E. (1988) *Agriculture–Health Linkages*, WHO Offset Publication 104, World Health Organization, Geneva.

McHale, J. & McHale, M. C. (1978) *Basic Human Needs: A Framework for Action*, Transaction Books, New Jersey.

Maclay, A. (1996) 'Simple and effective accounts', *Footsteps* **29**.

McPake, B., Hansen, K. & Mills, A. (1992) 'Implementing the Bamako Initiative in Africa: A Review and Five Case Studies', Policy and Health Planning departmental publication no. 8, London School of Hygiene and Tropical Medicine, London.

Mara, D. & Cairncross, S. (1989) *Guidelines for the Safe Use of Waste Water and Excreta in Agriculture and Aquaculture: Measures for Public Health Protection*, World Health Organization, Geneva.

Marlow, M. (1993) 'Malnutrition in elderly people – challenging the childhood bias', *The Health Exchange*, **Dec 1992–Jan 1993**.

Martin, J. (1992) 'Struggle against injustice', *Health Action* **2:** 4–5.

Martin, J. (1995) 'World Health Organization says better health needs more than the health sector', *Contact* **141**.

Masaka, J. S. (1993) abstract given at a global AIDS conference in Berlin.

Mason, P. (1990) *Tourism, Environment and Development Perspectives*, Worldwide Fund for Nature.

Mills, A. & Thomas, M. (1984) 'Economic Evaluation of Health Programmes in Developing Countries', Evaluation and Planning Centre publication 3, Winter, London School of Hygiene and Tropical Medicine, London.

Mitchell, P. A. (1996) 'Cost recovery can work', *Contact* **146:** 6–7.

Mukarji, D. (1996) 'Questioning the Robin Hood approach', *Contact* **146:** 9–11.

Mwesigye, R. F. (1994) 'Value for money', *Health Action* **9:** 6.

Myers, N. (1994) 'Eco-refugees – a crisis in the making', *People and Planet* **3**.

Najmi, K. & Harpham, T. (1992) 'From chronic emergency to development: an analysis of the health of the urban poor in Luanda, Angola', *International Journal of Health Services* **22:** 349–63.

National Council for International Health (1995) 'Violence as a Global Health Issue: Responding to the Crisis', National Council for International Health, June conference, Washington, DC.

Nduati, R. W. (1993) paper given at global AIDS conference in Berlin.

Newman, R. D. *et al.* (1993) 'Environmental sources of cryptosporidium in an urban slum in northeast Brazil', *American Journal of Tropical Medicine and Hygiene*, **49:** 270–75.

Nolan, B. & Turbat, V. (1993) *Cost Recovery in Public Health Services in Sub-Saharan Africa*, Human Resources Division, Economic Development Institute

Nunn, J. H. *et al.* (1992) 'Dental health of children in an integrated urban development programme for destitute mothers with twins in Addis Ababa', *International Dental Journal* **42**: 445–50.

Nyambura, J. 'Stolen childhood: common cause,' *Action Aid* **January–March:** 2–3.

Oakley, P. *et al.* (1991) *Projects with People: The Practice of Participation in Rural Development*, World Employment Programme, International Labour Office, Geneva.

ODA (1986) *Women in Development*, Information Dept, Overseas Development Administration, London.

ODA (1992a) *Action for the Environment*, Overseas Development Administration, London.

ODA (1992b) 'What do trees do – why are they important?' *Action for the Environment*, Overseas Development Administration, London, p. 18.

ODA (1995) article in *Overseas News*, Overseas Development Administration, London, July.

Oshima, H. T. (1990) 'Employment generation: the long-term solution to poverty', *Asian Development Review* **8**.

Owen, M. 'Widows banding together,' *People and Planet* **4**: 20–22.

Payne, K. (1993a) 'Health for all elderly people', *The Health Exchange* **December 1992–January 1993**.

Payne, K. (1993b) 'Older women lead the way!', *The Health Exchange* **December 1992–January 1993**.

People and Planet (1994) Issue entitled: 'Environmental refugees: a crisis in the making', *People and Planet* **3**.

Platt, A. (1995) 'Reversing our path to destruction', *People and Planet* **4**: 6–9.

Poore, P. (1993) personal correspondence, Save the Children, London.

Population Bulletin (1992) Issue entitled: 'Population and water resources: a delicate balance', *Population Bulletin* **47**.

Population Crisis Committee (1987) *The International Human Suffering Index*, Population Crisis Committee, Washington, DC.

Population Crisis Committee (1992) *The International Human Suffering Index*, Population Crisis Committee, Washington, DC.

Population Reports (1992) Issue entitled: 'The environment and population growth: decade for action', *Population Reports*, series M, no. 10.

Praphaphan, D. (1968) 'The curtain of affluence', *Contours* **2**.

Quibrera Infante, R. *et al.* (1994) 'Prevalencia de diabetes, intolerancia a la glucosa hiperlipermia y factores de riesgos en function de nivel socioeconomico', *Revista Invest. Clin* **46**: 25–36.

Rahman, A. *People's Self-development: Perspectives on Participatory Action Research*, Zed Books and London University Press, Dhaka, Bangladesh.

Ramaswamy, N. S. (1987) 'Draught animal power in developing countries with special reference to India', Animal production and health paper 42, Food and Agriculture Organization, Rome, pp. 140–43.

Ravaillon, M. (1991) 'The challenging arithmetic of poverty in Bangladesh', *Bangladesh Development Studies* **18**: 35–53.

Ravaillon, M. (1991) 'Reaching the poor through rural public employment: arguments, evidence and lessons from South Asia', *World Bank Research Observer*.

Renshaw, J. & Rivas, D. (1991) 'A community development approach to Chagas disease: the Sucre health project in Bolivia', *Health Policy and Planning* **6**: 244–53.

Rodgers, G. (ed.) (1995) *New Approaches to Poverty Analysis and Policy, Vol. 1 – The Poverty Agenda and the ILO: Issues for Research and Action* and *Vol. 2 – The Poverty Agenda: Trends and Policy Options*, International Institute and Labour Studies, International Labour Office, Geneva.

Rodgers, G. & Van der Hoeven, R, (eds) (1995) *New Approaches to Poverty Analysis and Policy, Vol 3 – The Poverty Agenda: Trends and Policy Options*, International Labour Office, Geneva.

Ron, A. & Kupferman (1996) *A Community Health Insurance Scheme in the Philippines: Extension of a Community-based Integrated Project*, World Health Organization, Geneva.

Rural Development Bulletin (1994) Issue entitled: 'Sustainable tourism', *Rural Development Bulletin* **5**.

Saha, E. (1996) 'HEED credit and loan systems', *Footsteps* **26**: 4–5.

Salem, C. (1996) 'When ducks pay the health bills', *Contact* **146**: 12–13.

Sanders, D. & Davies, R. (1988) 'Economic adjustment and current trends in child survival: the case of Zimbabwe', *Health Policy and Planning* **3**: 195–204.

Schorling, J. B. *et al.* (1990) 'Malnutrition is associated with increased diarrhoea incidence among children in an urban Brazilian slum', *International Journal of Epidemiology* **19**: 728–35.

Schwabe, C. (1981) 'Animal diseases and primary health care: intersectoral challenges', *WHO Chronicle* **35**: 227–32.

Senturias, E. N., 'God's mission and HIV/AIDS: shaping the churches' response', *International Review of Mission* **LXXXIII:** 277–84.

Simmons, P. (1995) *Words into Action: Basic Rights and the Campaign Against World Poverty*, Oxfam UK and Ireland, Oxford.

Sims, J. & Weinger, M. (1995) *Women, Health and Environment: A Teacher's Guide*, WHO/EHG/95, World Health Organization, Geneva.

Singha, P. P. & Ghosh, B. D. (1989) *Tackling Rural Poverty in India: Bundwan Shows the Way*, International Labour Organization, Geneva.

Smith-Pye, C. (1995) 'Salvation from sewage in Calcutta marshes', *People and Planet* **4:** 20–22.

Smyke, P. (1991) *Women and Health*, Zed Books, London.

South Asian Commission (1992) *Meeting the Challenge: Report of the Independent South Asian Commission on Poverty Alleviation*, South Asian Commission.

South–South Solidarity (1994a) *Urban Ecohealth*, South–South Solidarity, Bangalore, India.

South–South Solidarity (1994b) *A Global View of the Environment: Two Years After Rio*, South–South Solidarity, Bangalore, India.

Srilatha, V. & Aitken, I. W. (1991) 'A health risk index for assessing PHC coverage in urban India', *Health Policy and Planning* **6**: 234–43.

Stalker, P. (1994) *The Work of Strangers: A Survey of International Labour Migration*, International Labour Organization, Geneva.

Starkey, P. (1995) *Animal Traction in South Africa: Empowering Rural Communities*, Development Bank of South Africa.

Stephens, A. (1988) *Participatory Monitoring and Evaluation: Handbook for Training Field Workers*, Food and Agriculture Organization, Bangkok.

Stephens, B., Mason, J. & Isely, R. B. (1985) 'Health and low-cost housing', *World Health Forum* **6:** 59–62

Stephens, C. (1994) 'Health, Poverty and the Environment: The Nexus, an Overview Presentation', presented at the London School of Hygiene and Tropical Medicine.

Stephens, C. *et al.* (1994) 'Environment and Health in Developing Countries: An Analysis of Intra-urban Differentials in Accra, Ghana, Sao Paulo, Brazil, and Analysis of Urban Data in Ghana, Brazil, Egypt and Thailand', paper given at the London School of Hygiene and Tropical Medicine.

Stern, J. B. (1994) 'Poverty Reduction in Sierra Leone: A Framework for a National Action Plan', environment and social policy working paper ESP-03, African Development Bank, Abidjan, Cote d'Ivoire.

Streeten, P. (1995) *The Political Economy of Fighting Poverty*, International Labour Organization, Geneva.

Tabatabai, H. & Fouad, M. (1993) *The Incidence of Poverty in Developing Countries: An ILO Compendium of Data*, International Labour Organization, Geneva.

Tangcharoensathien, V. (1994) 'When people can't pay', *Health Action* **9:** 11.

TEAR Fund (1994) 'What happens to rubbish?', *Footsteps* **20**.

Tinker, A. I. *et al.* (1994) 'Women's Health and Nutrition: Making a Difference', World Bank discussion paper 256, World Bank, Washington, DC.

Tiroler, G. (1995) 'Learning about the links (poverty and disability)', *CBR News* **21:** 4–5.

UN (1989) *Report on the World Social Situation*, United Nations, New York.

UNAIDS (1996) personal communication to the author, UNAIDS, New York.

UNDP (1990) *Human Development Report*, United Nations Development Program, Oxford University Press, New York. (See also reports from 1991, 1992 and 1993.)

UNESC (1993) *The Poverty Situation in Asia and the Pacific*, Economic and Social Commission for Asia and the Pacific, United Nations Economic and Social Council, Bangkok.

UNICEF (1993a) *Education for All: Popular Participation, Mobilization and Decentralization for Education for All*, United Nations International Children's Emergency Fund, New York.

UNICEF (1993b) *Reaching the Unreached: Non-formal Approaches and Universal Primary Education*, United Nations International Children's Emergency Fund, New York.

UNICEF (1994) *The Progress of Nations: The Nations of the World, Ranked According to their Achievements in Child Health, Nutrition, Education, Family Planning and Progress*, United Nations International Children's Emergency Fund, New York.

UNICEF (1996) *The State of the World's Children*, United Nations International Children's Emergency Fund, New York.

UNRISD (1993) 'Rebuilding Wartorn Societies', report of workshops on the challenge of rebuilding wartorn societies and the social consequences of the peace process in Cambodia, United Nations Research Institute for Social Development, Geneva.

UNRISD (1995) 'Social Integration: Approaches and Issues', briefing paper series 1, United Nations Research Institute for Social Development, Geneva.

UNRISD (1996) *Wartorn Societies' Project Update* **1**: 4.

Vali (1984) *Rural–Urban Gap and Income Distribution (A Comparative Sub-regional Study): Synthesis Report of Seventeen African Countries*, International Labour Office and JASPA, Addis Ababa, Ethiopia.

Van Bergen (1994) 'District health care between quality assurance and crisis management', *Tropical and Geographical Medicine* **47**: 23–9.

Vella, V. *et al.* (1992) 'Determinants of child mortality in northwest Uganda', *Journal of Biosocial Science* **24**: 103–112.

Vogel, R. J. (1991) 'Cost recovery in public health services in sub-Saharan Africa', *International Journal of Health Planning and Management* **6**: 167–91.

Waddington, C. & Asiama, D. (1994) 'Making a drug fund work', *Health Action* **9**: 8.

Wadley, S. (1993) 'Family composition strategies', *Rural Science and Medicine* **37**: 1367–76.

Watkins, K. (1995) *The Oxfam Poverty Report*, Oxfam UK and Ireland, Oxford.

Werner, D. (1994) 'Turning Health Care Into an Investment: The Latest High-power Assaults on Primary Health Care', address to Churches' Action for Health, Pharmaceutical Advisory Group, Geneva.

Westen Dorf, D. G. & Ghai, D. (eds) (1993) *Monitoring Social Progress in the 1990s: Data Constraints, Concerns and Priorities*, Avebury (for UNRISD), Aldershot.

WGSAP (1995) Freedom from Debt and Working Group on Structural Adjustment Program, The Philippines.

Whittemore, C. (1981) *Land for People: Land Tenure and the Very Poor*, Oxfam Public Affairs Unit, Oxford.

WHO (1985) *Environmental Pollution Control in Relation to Development: Report of a WHO Expert Committee*, Technical Report series 718, World Health Organization, Geneva.

WHO (1989a) *Health Principles of Housing*, World Health Organization, Geneva.

WHO (1989b) *The Health of Youth*, A42/Technical Discussions/2, World Health Organization, Geneva.

WHO (1990a) *Cost Analysis in Primary Health Care: A Training Manual for Programme Managers*, WHO/SHS/NHP/90.5, Division of Strengthening of Health Services, World Health Organization, Geneva.

WHO (1990b) 'The poorest of the poor', *World Health*.

WHO (1992) *WHO Commission on Health and Environment: Report of the Panel on Urbanization*, World Health Organization, Geneva.

WHO (1993a) *AIDS Home Care Handbook*, WHO/GPA/IDS/HCS/93.2, World Health Organization, Geneva.

WHO (1993b) *Planning and Implementing Health Insurance in Developing Countries: Guidelines and Case Studies*, Macroeconomic, Health and Development series, World Health Organization, Geneva.

WHO (1994a) *Action for Children Affected by AIDS: Programme Profiles and Lessons Learned*, World Health Organization and UNICEF, Geneva.

WHO (1994b) Issue entitled: 'Health care is homeward bound', *World Health*.

WHO (1994c) *Improving Access to Credit for the Poor: A Review of Experiences*, Joint WHO–IBRD Workshop on 'Banking for Health, WHO/DGH/ICO/BfH/94.4, World Health Organization, Geneva.

WHO (1994d) *Protocol for the Study of Interpersonal Physical Abuse of Children*, WHO/FHE/CHD/94.1, Division of Family Health, World Health Organization, Geneva.

WHO (1994e) *Public Health and Coastal Tourism (Sea, Tourism, Health)*, WHO/EOS/94.39, World Health Organizations, Geneva.

WHO (1994f) Issue entitled: 'Reaching out to the poorest', *World Health*.

WHO (1994g) *Symptom Glossary for Mental Disorders*, WHO/MNH/MND/94.11, Division of Mental Health, World Health Organization, Geneva.

WHO (1995a) *Health in Social Development: WHO Position Paper*, given at the World Summit for Social Development in Copenhagen, World Health Organization, Geneva.

WHO (1995b) *The World Health Report, 1995 – Bridging the Gaps*, World Health Organization, Geneva.

WHO (1996a) *A Community Health Insurance Scheme in the Philippines: Extension of a Community-based Integrated Project*, Macroeconomic, Health and Development series, World Health Organization, Geneva.

WHO (1996b) *TB Deaths Reach Historic Levels*, press release WHO/22, 21 March, World Health Organization, Geneva.

WHO (1996c) *Water and Sanitation*, WHO Fact Sheet 112, March, World Health Organization, Geneva.

WHO (1996d) *WHO Calls for Strengthening Nursing Profession*, press release WHO/7, paper 2, 24 May, World Health Organization, Geneva.

World Bank (1990) *World Development Report – Better Health in Africa: Experience and Lessons Learned*, Oxford University Press, Oxford. (See also report from 1994.)

World Bank (1992) *China: Strategies for Reducing Poverty in the 1990s*, report no. 10409-cha, Washington, DC.

World Bank (1993a) *Implementing the World Bank's Strategy to Reduce Poverty: Progress and Challenges*, World Bank, Washington, DC.

World Bank (1993b) *Poverty Reduction Handbook*, World Bank, Washington, DC.

World Bank (1993c) *World Development Report: Investing in Health*, Oxford University Press, Oxford.

World Bank (1994a) *Making Development Sustainable: The World Bank Group and the Environment*, World Bank, Washington, DC.

World Bank (1994b) *Zambia: Poverty Assessment, vol. 5: Participatory Poverty Assessment*, Southern African Department, Africa Regional Office, World Bank, Washington, DC.

World Bank (1995) *Viet Nam: Poverty Assessment and Strategy*, Country Operations Division, Country Department 1, East Asia and Pacific Region, World Bank, Washington, DC.

World Council of Churches, 'Accelerated Climate Change: Signs of Peril, Test of Faith', study paper, World Council of Churches, Geneva.

Yaron, J. (1994) 'What makes rural finance institutions successful?', *The World Bank Research Observer* **9**: 49–70.

INDEX

quality indicators 173
Quibebra Infante, R. 38

rainforests 126
rape 92
rat control 80
reafforestation 123, 155
refugees, eco 138
refuse collection 43
relevance indicators 172
Renshaw, J. 62
reports, for poverty profiling 21
reproductive health 56, 91
resource mapping 27
restaurants, low-cost 145, 147
revolving funds 102, 104, 166–7
Rivas, D. 62
Ron, A. 167
roofing 43
ROSCAs 102
rubbish disposal 119
Russell, S. 161

Safe Motherhood Initiative 50, 116
safety nets, social 139–44
sanitation 43, 46, 63, 81–2
schistosomiasis 45
schools, food schemes 145–6
Schwabe, C. 79
screens for doors/windows 43, 81
seasonality
  disease 27
  food 26, 37
  living standards 13
  water supply 128
security 142
sewage 46, 130, 133
sex tourism 94–5
sexually transmitted diseases 47, 55, 95,
  151–2
shanty towns: see slums
shellfish 133
shelter 9, 10, 39–43, 81, 142
sick, productivity 116–17
slavery 31–2, 110
slums 31, 37, 39, 44
Smith 132
Smyke, P. 59
social decay 137–8
social insurance 141
social mapping 25
social welfare, lack of access 75
Society for Promotion of Area Resource,
  Bombay 40
soil erosion 30, 123–4
solidarity 103, 147
Solomon Islands 105
South Africa 40, 60, 62
spiritual needs 9, 10
squatter settlements: see slums
Sri Lanka 143–4, 145
Srilatha, V. 14
Ssemulassa, M. 153
Stalker, P. 33
Stephens, A. 176, 177, 180

Stephens, C. 55, 60
street children 55–6, 64
stress assessment 153–5
structural adjustment 69, 143–4
subsidies 69, 143–4
substance abuse 54, 55, 91
surveys, community/household 20
survival patterns 114–15, 116–17
sustainable development 121–2

taboos, food 38
Tangcharoensathien, V. 162
targeting indicators 143–4
task monitoring 176
technical support, monitoring 183
technology
  appropriate 80–6
  lack of access 28, 69–70
  for survival 169
Thailand 162
time lines 26
Tiroler, G. 157
tourism 94–6
traditional birth attendant 50, 83
transport 10
tuberculosis 37, 62–3
Turbot 160

Uganda 24, 52, 151–3, 159, 161
UNAIDS 150, 152
underemployment 66–7
UNDP, water 44
unemployment 28, 33, 66–8
UNICEF 165
United Kingdom, poverty 17
United Nations
  Earth Summit 121–2
  Safe Motherhood Initiative 50
United Nations Commission for Refugees
  92
United Nations Environmental Programme
  123
United Nations Fund for Population
  Activities 120
UNRISD 137
urbanisation 30–1
user fees 160–2
utilisation indicators 172

Van Bergen 161
Vella, V. 52
ventilation 43
vets, barefoot 78–9
Viet Nam 175
violence
  conflict 135–7
  death 55, 136
  domestic 74, 91
  from exploitation 74
  external 74
  human rights 70
  and poverty 53, 57
  rape 92
Vogel 160
voting 28, 70

vulnerability
  elderly 57–8
  environmental 30, 71, 134–5
  poverty 7–9
  shelter 41

Waddington, C. 167
Wadley, S. 50
war 29, 73, 135–7
warning systems, disasters 156
waste disposal 42
water
  access 75, 129
  aquifers 121, 128
  for drinking 42–4, 75, 141–2
  drought 29, 123–4
  and health 43
  hygiene 44, 82
  pollution 34, 129, 130–2
  poverty 45–6
  shortage 81–2, 128–9
  storage 44
  technology 81–2
water-borne disease 44–5, 75
wealth distribution, inequalities 28, 29, 66
wealth ranking 24
weaning 37
welfare state 141
well-being 24
WHO 44, 53, 55, 61, 62, 63, 150
wildlife, habitats 127–8
women
  abused 29
  circumcision 48
  credit repayments 102–3
  employment 95, 145
  health care 41, 57, 58, 82–3
  housing loans 40
  income and family health 10, 105
  inequalities 29
  land rights 91
  livestock 77–8
  nutrition 116
  older 59
  rights over income 151
  wage levels 67
  water supplies 44, 45
  widows 91
  see also maternal mortality
Women's World Banking 104
workplace: see occupational health
World Bank 15, 24, 159
worms 45, 54, 63

Yanomami people 34
Year of the Family 115
Yemen, livestock extension programme
  78

Zambia 146, 150, 151
Zapatista National Liberation Army
  108–9
Zimbabwe 105, 148, 165
zoonoses 79–80